D0541669

A Farmer's Lot . . .

A Farmer's Lot . . .

Fordyce Maxwell

Illustrated by Graham Lang

Bridge Studios
Northumberland
1988

First published in Great Britain in 1988

by Bridge Studios,
   4B Bridge Street,
   Morpeth,
   Northumberland,
   NE61 1NB.

   Tel. 0670 518101/519561

ISBN 0 9512630 6 4

Printed in Great Britain by
Martins of Berwick

For Susie

Acknowledgements

The stories in this anthology are reproduced by kind permission of the *Newcastle Journal*, the *Scotsman*, the *Glasgow Herald* and the *Scottish Farmer*.

Foreword

Farming is a serious business. The kind of farmer who is born old and spends the rest of his life getting older likes to tell me this.

They needn't. I know. Anyone born and raised as the oldest of nine children on a smallish family farm knows it is a serious and often precarious way to make a living.

But you have to laugh at the way farming hits back when you think you're in control, at the foibles of farmers in general and ourselves in particular.

I'm thankful for many things about my father, but most of all for encouraging me to see the funny side of farming. Not everyone did, as I found during a mis-spent education – two years working at home and two years at college.

The discouragement became more marked after I received an award as the student who had done most for the college – I left – and became a journalist for ten years.

During this time of looking at farming from the outside, my natural cynical streak became a broad band. I saw truth in many forms at farmers' meetings, at shows, at sales and on the farms I visited. I was redirected to the tradesman's entrance by a butler at one and helped chase hens out of the kitchen at another.

I listened with interest to what leaders of the industry said in private compared with what they said publicly and wondered, without malice, how they managed to lie straight in bed.

I heard what was said about men when they were alive compared with the eulogies when they died, compared pedigree prices with commercial prices, compared what the National Farmers' Union said about the Government with what the Government said about the National Farmers'

Union and compared it all with what my father was doing.

I reported the truth as I saw it and occasionally poked a little fun. One day at the Highland show, as I tried to disentangle fact from fiction in the Beef Shorthorn prize list, a member of the farming hierarchy approached.

He eyed me sombrely. Eventually he spoke:

'Every time you write you devalue farming,' he said.

'Every time?' I squawked.

'Every time,' he said bitterly and strode off to be hospitable to Royalty.

He was too late. Only weeks after I became a journalist I was introduced to a meeting I was reporting as 'the lad who made a right mess of Perth ram sales report'.

This assessment of a journalist's place in the scheme of things was on a par with the advice I got when leaving journalism to go back to full time farming, that I would certainly be as well shovelling it as writing it!

Or the conversation I overheard at Kelso ram sales. That morning a piece had appeared in the paper taking a humorous dig at pedigree breeding and I was modestly content.

One farmer describing this article to the other said:

'Do you think Fordyce Maxwell's the bugger's real name anyway?'

The second farmer replied:

'Is Fordyce Maxwell whose real name?'

It is this encouragement which keeps me going, the belief that no matter how hard I try someone will hate it.

Sometimes I try to humour these serious people by writing about the serious side of the business, easy enough in these parlous times.

More often I take a wry look at the lighter side, the side which is reflected most often in this selection.

People say that farmers aren't funny. They make *me* laugh.

No substitute for experience

'Right,' said the interviewer wearily, 'send in number 17. Please sit down, Mr Havelock.

'Now,' he went on, gazing hopefully at the cryptic, typewritten note in front of him perched as it was on a mound of college and national diplomas and reams of fulsome character references provided by the previous 16 applicants, 'let's not waste each other's time.

'Do you know anything about running a 600-acre livestock and arable farm successfully?'.

'Very little,' said Havelock, preparing to rise from his chair.

'Good,' said the interviewer, heaving a sigh of relief and sitting back. 'Oh, good. You really do sound as if you've had experience – the job's yours.

'Here,' he said, 'have a cigar, or would you care for a drink while we discuss the details of salary and so on. But first, is there anything you'd like to ask?'

'Well, yes,' Havelock murmured. 'If you don't mind me saying so, that's rather an unusual selection procedure you adopted there. I mean, I say I really know very little about running your type of farm – or any type come to that – successfully and you say, good, you've got the job. How come?'

'I'm glad you asked,' said the interviewer, pouring himself a stiff treble, 'very glad indeed. You got the job, if you really want it of course, because as I said you sound like a man who's had experience.

'You wouldn't believe,' he continued, settling himself comfortably and taking a brisk pull at his whisky, 'you simply wouldn't believe what I've gone through in this room this morning.

'Sixteen fresh-faced enthusiasts with their heads stuffed full

3

of theory and their briefcases stuffed full of diplomas and references all anxious to tell me how they'll give me a £200,000 turnover and £50,000 profit.'

'Ah, now, be fair,' said Havelock, 'we were all like that once. I know I was, and somebody had to give us a chance to learn.'

'But,' said Havelock's new employer, 'were you really as super-confident as these lads seem to be. Why try and promise the impossible then give yourself ulcers for the next five years wondering why it hasn't worked out?'

'Because,' said Havelock, 'at that age it doesn't seem impossible. For two years, or three years, or whatever they do now at college, you've been stuffed with facts and figures, gross margins and cash flows, the crops you decide to sow on paper all give the yields you estimate they'll give, livestock don't die, it doesn't rain at harvest, machinery doesn't break down, workers don't fall ill, or leave suddenly, the bank manager doesn't turn nasty, the Government doesn't allow cheap imports to flood the market, new buildings go up on time at the cost they were supposed to go up for – oh, lots of things work out just fine on paper.

'And I know,' he went on reflectively, sipping his drink, 'because I used to do well in college management exercises. Why, I remember once working out on paper that in the first year of taking over a run-down farm I could make a handsome profit from a set of derelict old buildings by filling them with 2000 turkeys, packing them in at a bird per two square feet.

'Apart from the fact that one-half would have eaten the other half by Christmas, I never actually worked out how I was going to pluck them single-handed. But, my word, it was impressive on paper – that was worth a credit.

'Not to mention,' he said, his shoulders shaking gently, 'that I once gave it, as my gratuitous opinion on a farm we visited, that any plan I prepared for it could be nothing but an improvement on what the old goat farming it was doing. I suppose I should have guessed he was on the college board of governors and a close friend of the principals.'

'Well, I suppose you've got a point,' said the interviewer, refilling his glass, 'but if that system's what gives these lads such inflated ideas, don't you think the system should be changed?'

'Oh, indubitably,' said Havelock, mellowing a little more with each sip, 'indubitably. What's really needed is a down to earth examination. I've thought about it, you know.

'For example, I toyed with a few sample questions. How about this one to take their minds off fancy theories. It's a scorching day in the middle of harvest and you're helping the man in the drier clear a blocked auger when the tractor driver appears in a cloud of dust to murmur conversationally that the half-shaft on your new combine has broken. On your way to inspect the damage you notice 20 bulling heifers careering round the wheat field and a leisurely procession of 200 mule ewes making for the turnips. At this point the van you're driving gets a flat tyre.

'Do you (a) light a cigarette and count up to 2000; (b) head off the ewes; (c) throw stones at the heifers; (d) drive on the wheel rims; (e) shoot yourself?'

'Interesting,' murmured the interviewer. 'What did you do?'

'Ah, that was hypothetical,' said Havelock. 'I've had the sheep and the cattle separately, but never together. But how about this one.

'After a morning during which a load of barley has been rejected for malting and you've had a friendly chat with the graders about 30 lambs, the bank manager rings at lunchtime. You are £4000 above your overdraft limit. Do you (a) murmur sweet nothings about a cheque for 50 tons of barley being on its way; (b) mention that the pheasant shooting prospects look good this year; (c) put on a falsetto voice and say Mr Havelock is critically ill and not to be disturbed for three weeks?'

'And?' said the interviewer.

'Something to be said for all three,' said Havelock. 'Personally I prefer the 50 tons of barley, but it's a matter of preference and would give you an insight into the way the candidate's mind works. A falsetto voice could be quite an asset in certain circumstances.'

'It's a good idea, you know,' said the interviewer, 'very good. You should try to get it adopted – much more realistic than working out the best substitute or replacement for oats in an arable rotation based on gross margins.'

'I think so,' said Havelock modestly, 'and how about asking them to describe in not more than 25 words the net impact of the Common Agricultural Policy allied to domestic Government policy on the future of British farming. If they took more than three words, they fail.'

'You know,' said the interviewer, gazing almost fondly on Havelock, 'I think we're going to get along very well. When can you start?'

Nothing funny about a bunny

'Right, Dad, guess what we've got in the box?'
'A goldfish.'
'Aw, don't be silly. The goldfish is there in the bowl.'
'Well, that's all you went for wasn't it? (Pause). Wasn't it?'
'Right, sort of. But we got something else. So guess what's in the box.'
'Ahm hmm – Tortoise? Hamster? Gerbil? Tarantula? Grass snake? Tiger? Leopard?'
'It's a WHAT!'
'R..r..rabbit. Why are you saying it like that. Mum, why is he smashing up the furniture? Why is he going that funny colour?'
'A rabbit?'
'He's coming round the back green again, Mum, we'll catch him this time.'
'The rabbit?'
'No, Dad – here he comes.'
'Just calm down, dear. Stand there and clutch that tree. That's right.'
'A rabbit!'
'Why does he keep saying that, Mum?'
'I think he may have been taken by surprise, pet.'
'A rabbit!'
'Well, what's wrong with a rabbit? It's little and brown.'
'A little brown rabbit! We've got ten thousand of them out there. They've eaten 20 acres of winter barley and half a forest already this winter. I spend weeks each year killing the little b..bb...brown beggars and . . .'
'I think he's passed out again, Mum.'
'Oh lord, what were you thinking of? A rabbit. A little brown rabbit. The perfect farm pet. Thank you lord, thank you.'

'Will he lie on his back waving his legs in the air for long, Mum.'

'The rabbit?'

'No, Dad.'

'It's all right he's getting up now and tottering over here. That's right, have a cup of coffee and relax.'

'What were you thinking about? I'd rather have a white rat on the place.'

'I don't know why you're so upset, Dad.'

'Look at it this way. We've had goldfish before. One lasted half an hour before doing a double back flip out of a dish that was too shallow for it and expiring on the carpet. Where I stood on it.'

'We've got a proper bowl this time and proper food and proper pebbles and..'

'Good. In that case I give it two days. We have a cat. I grant you it's a better cat than I thought it would be. It's mewing and scraping at the window at four in the morning leave something to be desired and it costs as much to feed as a small bullock, but never mind. It does kill mice as well as birds and the occasional SMALL RABBIT!'

'Oh, don't be so horrible.'

'It does. It's a good cat that now I come to think of it. Seldom seen a better. It'll be out there now eyeing up that rabbit beyond the chicken wire.'

'Don't say things like that to the bairn. She's gone white.'

'*She's* gone white. I've gone grey in the space of ten minutes. I'll be the laughing stock. I spend days on end gassing and shooting and ferreting the little beggars and now, at my back door in a hutch – it doesn't bear thinking about.'

'Oh don't be so melodramatic. It's a dwarf rabbit. It was only £3.50 – stop clutching your heart like that.'

'Three pounds fifty. Oh death, where is thy sting. Three pounds fifty for a dwarf brown rabbit. Where's my gun?'

'You're not going to shoot it?'

'No, I'm going to shoot whoever sold it to you. Either that or set up in business. It beats oilseed rape or pigs. Dwarf brown rabbits for sale – get your dwarf brown rabbits here – place your orders now – dwarf b . .'

8

'Did he mean to fall over that cat, Mum?'
'I think I'll go and start the tea.'
'Fur gloves for sale – black and white fur gloves . . .'

Over-rated miracle?

Dear diary – This is it, this is the big one. My first lambing after two years as a veterinary student. I can hardly wait to put all my knowledge into practice. This seems like a nice place and the farmer says he has a canny dog I can use any time I need one. But all the ewes are inside now anyway, waiting for the miracle of birth. I'm so thrilled.

Dear diary – Well, that's my first day. It wasn't quite what I expected, but it was interesting, I don't think that the dog is quite as good as the farmer said. We were loading the last of the hoggs for the mart this morning – he thought I'd be as well to get a bit of all-round sheep experience – and the collie bit one of them. Actually, I thought he was going to eat it, but the farmer gave him a playful poke with his foot and he stopped.

In fact he stopped doing anything for a few minutes, but he seems all right now – he's just bitten the postman. I was in charge of the ewes while the farmer went to see the hoggs graded. He poked the dog playfully with his foot again when he came back. He said he was going to write to the Training Board to get a course run on rubber-ringing graders. I'm not sure what he meant.

Dear diary – Things are speeding up a bit now. Two pairs, a three, a single and a prolapse during the night. I try to be as gentle as I can when I have to help the ewe because the farmer says these ewes are just not used to rough treatment. Handle them gently at all times, he said, and was quite firm about it.

I'm doing my best, but the three was a bit of a problem – just a mixture of legs, heads and tails and I kept getting the wrong bit out. But I managed all on my own and they seem to be doing fine. The prolapse was a bit tricky too – it seemed

10

straightforward enough in the drawings in the textbook, but there wasn't much blood and muck about there. Once I got the bits of straw off and put some antiseptic cream on I got it back quite well. Gosh, I'm tired.

Dear diary – When I got to the shed this morning, the farmer had the ewe with the prolapse standing on her head while he put it back in place again. I did think it wasn't very gentle, but he said you sometimes had to be cruel to be kind. Feeding a lamb with a tube isn't bad, but getting a weak one to suck from a bottle is a bit tricky. They dribble and slobber all over. The farmer said patience is the only way with them.

Dear diary – Several more ewes lambed today. Most are fine except a premature pair that are soft and wobbly and won't drink. I'm almost certain they're nearly an abortion, but the farmer says this farm has never had an abortion problem – never even had one case of it.

He must be unique in this part of the world, but got quite insistent about it. He said clutching a weak lamb by the throat was the only way to get it to drink – its eyes were popping, but it still didn't seem to drink much. I coaxed some milk into it when he'd gone. Feel tired.

Dear diary – Haven't written anything for three days. Bit of a blur really. About 50 ewes have lambed. I had an exact total, but the farmer used the sheet of paper to rub down a lamb that wouldn't breathe. I said he might have used something else and he said he'd used everything else from a piece of hay to his cap.

He was trying to give it the kiss of life after swinging it round his head when he said this. I asked what was wrong with it and he said a naughty word. But I'm learning all the time. Shattered.

Dear diary – Five days since I managed to note my progress. About 80 ewes have lambed. Think 60 of them were in one night. Hard to keep track. Ewes have same trouble. At one time found four ewes with nine lambs. All lambed in same corner within 20 minutes. I think. Farmer wasn't convinced. One ewe claimed seven of them, another would have nothing to do with any of them.

Put her in home-made lamb-adopter where she kicked the

stuffing out of two lambs until farmer hit her over the head with a plastic bucket, which broke. He asked me to go and check a ewe which looked like lambing in the far away pen while he looked after this little problem. When I got back he was breathing heavily and he seemed to have broken his crook.

Found that ewes housed inside get very lazy. Sometimes they just drop a lamb and don't even bother to lick off the membrane. If several are lambing at the same time in different pens I have to move pretty smartly to keep a check on them all. Exhausted.

Dear diary – Down to last 25 ewes after three weeks of non-stop work. I may be humpty-backed for life. Think I cracked a rib some time ago leaning over a hurdle, but haven't had time to check. Breathing with difficulty. Farmer taking large swigs of Miracle Lamb Reviver in past few days. Says it's no bloody good for lambs, but maybe it'll help him.

Days dragging a bit – still 17 to lamb. Last eight have produced five singles, one three, one hung lamb, one dead ewe. Discovered this morning that I'd rubber-ringed two tup lambs he was going to keep. He said they were pedigree. He said several other things I didn't like very much. When he tried to cut the ring off one and slit his finger I wasn't sorry. The miracle of birth is over-rated.

Dear diary – Last day here. He's still got five to lamb. Last 12 have produced eight singles, one hung, set of quads the size of hamsters and a giant pair. Also one dead ewe. One of the giant pair hung itself in the hay rack. The ewe lay on the other. I'm so thrilled to be going.

Dear diary – Home at last. Bed. Bath. Clean clothes. No sheep. No sheep at all. Left on fairly good terms, with a bottle of Miracle Lamb Reviver for the journey and a nip from the dog. Gave it a playful poke with my foot. Lift to the bus with the kennels van. Learnt a lot. May specialise in small animal surgery. Absolutely tired out.

Having the blast word

Anyone, by which I mean everyone, getting out of a car or lorry at the top of our hill, says the same thing, namely: 'Bit blowy up here,' 'Bit draughty,' 'Dear me, what a gale,' and so on.

There have been even more 'dear me's' than usual during the gales of the past week as we walk around with a permanent lean into the wind, breathless, and in constant danger of decapitation by slamming doors and flying roof sheets.

There is a poem dealing with this kind of weather which of course I can't remember. It goes something like 'there is grandeur in the growling of the gale' and 'beauty in the bellow of the blast'.

That may be true for a poet, but not so apt if you're actually trying to work in it and climbing in and out of a tractor door without losing a few fingers is a major effort.

There are those who claim that every problem is simply a solution in disguise. These positive thinkers suggest that our super-abundance of wind could be put to good use by converting it to electricity.

The theory is quite good. I've seen these modern windmills with their aerodynamically designed trio of blades. I'm not quite sure what that phrase means, but they use it in the promotional literature, so it must be true.

The idea is that you select one to suit your requirements, build it on the kind of exposed site which we can provide so readily and sell any surplus electricity to the national grid. Nothing could be simpler.

There are two drawbacks. One, inevitably, is money. I saw two of the biggest models in Aberdeenshire which seem to work well, but cost more than £40,000 each. The smallest models cost about £15,000.

The second drawback is that I've had limited experience with windmills. At least we called it a windmill; it was actually a type of windpump which used to be quite common in this part of the world before we got the mixed blessing of mains water.

The windpump was probably about 20 feet high, like a small electricity pylon with a metal-vaned wheel on top which spun round. It also swung to catch the wind from whichever direction it was blowing.

The wind blew, the vaned wheel spun, the pumping rod drove up and down, and the water flowed up the pipes to the storage tanks at the farm.

The rate at which the wheel spun could be controlled by a wire cable attached to a handle at the bottom. Sometimes in a gale this handle would slip or the cable would snap and the pump would go berserk.

As the pumping rod was of fairly basic construction, wooden strips bolted together, it couldn't take too much of this. A sedate up and down every 20 seconds was all right, but when the gale drove it on to 60 plunges per minute splinters started flying off.

If help was at hand, the idea was to pull the handle back into the off position. I have so many happy memories of hauling down and swinging on the handle, trying to get it back into place before the windpump shook itself to pieces.

If the cable snapped or the pumping rod finally broke there was nothing to do, but leave it until the gale blew itself out.

At the opposite extreme, unlikely though it seems to me now, there were periods of calm. The wind did not blow, the wheel did not turn and the water did not flow.

At times like this, it was peaceful and pleasant to climb to the top of the pump and look for bare patches in the barley, while the water was pumped by flat belt on a tractor pulley.

The alternative to that was a two-stroke engine, a particularly vicious specimen of equipment. I've always thought that whoever invented two-stroke engines should be condemned to pull the starting cord on one for ever, with the

14

spark plug removed.

Every time the cord snapped to split his hand, graze his knuckles or dislocate his wrist, a new one would be fitted and he could start again. Two-stroke engines deserve a chapter of their own in any farming history and the one we used on the windpump deserves its own page.

Taking it all in, I preferred the wind and the gales. Considering how I feel about them, that says it all.

I've no doubt that the modern windmills are a different proposition. They look sleek and efficient. The theory is good and the wind is free. But I have a long memory and still have my doubts.

The crazy world of fowl play

You may have heard that record: 'My father had a rabbit and he thought it was a duck . . .'

We used to have a duck that thought it was a Harrier jump jet. It was one of a long line of farmyard fowl eccentrics we had around the place over the years.

Now there are few hens pecking about and leaving little messages just where you put your hand, aimed at convincing the casual visitor that they're in a traditional farmyard and deigning to lay eggs now and again.

But at one time most farmyards had fowl and we were no exception. The geese were the worst – big flippers trailing mud everywhere and squirting several square feet at a time like giant seagulls.

Not only that, geese tend to be vicious. No wonder they became unpopular, racing about with their necks stretched out and beaks open, hissing and nipping.

There was a technique to handle these attacks. It was to wait until the goose was almost on you then, like some big game snake hunter, grab it by the neck just behind the head.

Once caught, the goose was swung around energetically several times then dropped to the ground to totter off dizzy and unsteady.

I use the past tense because I'm not sure what the views of the animal rights people would be on protecting yourself from a crazed goose attack, but no doubt some people still use this ancient method with success.

Cockerels, particularly bantam cockerels, also seemed to be particularly aggressive.

We had one which matched its aggressiveness with cunning by waiting until your arms were full or a bag or bale was being carried, then launching itself like a hawk.

16

There's not a lot of eating on a bantie cockerel, but it tasted quite good if rather sinewy.

Turkeys, as with anything else they do, were too stupid to be much of a nuisance when we kept a few from one Christmas to the next.

It was a half-hearted attempt at breeding, but they couldn't even get the hang of that; they just wandered about looking for somewhere comfortable to hang, drown or otherwise do away with themselves. It seemed to pass the time.

Of the ducks, I preferred the darting little Khaki Campbells to the bigger, more ponderous, even sillier, white Aylesburys.

Khaki Campbells, mud brown and nondescript, also laid many more eggs. It was a pity that after the rearing, caring and build-up to the great event of the first egg, no one actually cared much for them.

Duck eggs are yellow, rich and rather rubbery, good for baking but not so attractive in an egg cup although that's just my opinion. Everyone else seemed to share it.

The real off-beats of the duck world are the Muscovys with their peculiar red face covering which always reminds me of a hard drinker with a bottle nose like W. C. Fields.

They don't seem to go in much for egg-laying, or anything else for that matter, but it was a Muscovy which decided it was a Harrier jump jet.

It started modestly enough by flipping up onto a low wall and graduated to landing on the house roof. From there, came the highlight of his performance, when he zoomed down and landed on the narrow beam which separated two open dog runs.

This was a hazardous manoeuvre any Harrier pilot would have been glad to avoid. We had collies on either side at the time which went crazy each time the Muscovy did his party trick.

It wasn't so much the landing, it was the way the duck sat looking down at them which drove them frantic. One became expert at climbing the wire netting vertically and frothing at the mouth, but couldn't quite manage the last few inches.

The expression on its face as it began to slide back down the netting, paws scrabbling, teeth clacking like castanets and emitting howls of pure frustration had to be seen to be appreciated.

The old collie, Nap, who may have seen similar feathered show offs in a long and sinful life, growled below, but did not get too frantic. He knew, as we knew, that one day the duck would miscalculate.

He did. We didn't see it, but we knew by the joyful yelps. Quickly on the scene, but not quickly enough, we found a pair of duck feet. It got an entry in the diary:
'Accidental death – overshot the runway.'

Memories are made of this

A neatly wrapped selection of pork cuts prepared by the butcher for the freezer is all very well, but it's not the same as a pig killing is it?

I suppose it is one of the many changes which seem to have foreshortened the past 30 years or so since a pig killing used to be a semi-social occasion enjoyed by all – except possibly the pig.

These occasions also proved the theory that everything about a pig can be used except the squeal. Anyone who has played headers or keepie-up with a dried pig's bladder can testify to that; we made our own fun in those days.

Memory of course is subjective. I'm always suspicious of people with alleged total recall who write books about the good old days.

I like to think I have a good memory, but when possible to check it against a written record it is not infallible. My opinion is that what we call memory is really a blend of impressions at the time and what we have been told, read or seen since.

We had an example of it recently in this paper with the debate about whether barefoot children were seen in the Newcastle of the 1920s. Which is by way of saying that my own tender-age impressions of a pig killing may differ from yours, if you ever attended one.

Not everyone did, even when pigs were much more common on farms and in village and town pigsties than they are now. Feeding them on a variety of swill and meal was one thing, actually disposing of them for ready meat was another.

Each locality seemed to have its own specialist who appeared on the day to dispatch the unfortunate guffie, in my earliest memory with a heavy wooden mallet then more humanely in later years with a rifle shot.

In these days of creeping vegetarianism and genuine disquiet about some methods of ritual slaughter still in use, the pig killing as we knew it may seem barbaric.

As I said earlier, it is a sign of how times change that that thought never crossed our mind as the barely-deceased was shot, slung up on the tripod, the throat was cut and blood collected for black pudding making and the innards removed and carefully separated and arranged for later use.

There was a big wooden tub with boiling water and a vigorous scrubbing and scraping of the sides which were to become bacon. These would either be salted and hung or sweet-cured to give a softer cut.

Anyone who has eaten home-cured thick-fat bacon will remember it. If you haven't there is no point in trying to describe the unique, salty, greasy flavour of this heartburn special.

But that was later. On the day there was immediate fare in the shape of pig's liver and spareribs cooking in the oven. On the fairly-soon list for the next few days were black and white puddings, potted meat and sausages.

Making these was where my grandfather, who had trained as a butcher before becoming a railwayman for the rest of his working life, came into his own.

I know there are still good traditional butchers about, but when most sausages these days are plastic skinned it is possible to think that the skills of my grandfather have gone.

He would wash and scrape meticulously clean the intestines to make his sausage skins. Then feed his mixture of meat and he alone knew what else into the mincer with the sausage making attachment.

As the skin filled he would put the twists in at the right time to produce sausage links. It was something I could watch for hours, and probably did until I was old enough to be kept busy doing something else.

For all the time I spent watching and, despite my best efforts, I could never make sausages myself; they came off the manual assembly line misshapen, twisted and humpy

backed Quasimodos of the banger world. But they tasted just as good.

Ah well, it was a long time ago and memory is subjective. Like footballers, the sausages of our youth seemed a lot better than those of today, particularly the home-made ones.

A freezer pack just isn't the same although it is a thought that that is what our own children will have to remember from their formative years. Not much is it?

It's hard, working to scale

Like a good farm a good garden is a place of steady change as one operation blends into the next. There is always a sense of progress and movement as crops and flowers come and go in their season. Or so I'm told.

I've never had a good garden. Very few farmers have unless they pay or coerce someone else into doing it for them.

That is not quite true. For a month or two in the year a farm garden will look tidy. Then work on the farm gets into top gear again and the garden slowly slips back towards the wild from which it was recently reclaimed.

That tidy month or two is with us as the strain of lambing eases and with crop work completed as well as it can be except for the sprayer always ready for action.

At last with the only alternatives being to spring clean the steading or start painting and creosoting the farmer turns towards his garden.

It is not a pretty sight. The good gardener, like the good farmer, begins his cropping preparations well in advance with steady digging in the autumn.

The bad gardener, who may well be a good enough farmer, begins his preparations in late April by grabbing a spade in a bad temper and digging in a frenzy until his back seizes up.

That is only if the garden is so badly designed that a tractor or plough can't be brought in to turn over the soil.

This difference in scale is part of if not the whole problem. A man used to dealing with 20 acre fields with a four furrow plough does not take kindly to a garden which has to be dug by hand.

Although it may seem small compared with a field a farm garden is usually big compared with other gardens. It takes a long time to dig and prepare and allowances should be made for this.

Instead the farmer will adopt the blitzkrieg approach of trying to do it in three nights before collapsing and become progressively more thwarted as he fails to manage it.

Gardening should be relaxation. It can be when there is no battle against the clock or even the calendar.

But when it should have been dug several weeks ago if not months and crops should be through the ground and thriving rather than being ripped out of their packets and pushed in furiously, it is hard to relax.

Fertiliser which would be carefully calibrated at three or three and a half cwts an acre in the field will be flung on in generous handfuls or by the half bucket in the general flurry of activity.

This is in the vegetable part of the garden. If he has to garden at all the average farmer will work with vegetables. Work on the flower garden will only be done under duress and more importantly supervision.

This is necessary because a man who can recognise seven different varieties of spring barley while growing, knows the name and nature of 29 different sprays and can identify 43 different breeds and crosses of sheep cannot tell the difference between chickweed and pansies or any other combination of weed and flower.

If asked to tidy the flower garden this generally means yanking out any greenery above ground level and remarking the resulting expanse of bare soil 'looks tidy'.

Only healthily growing shrubs of two feet high or more, preferably with thorns like roses or pyracantha, are safely recognisable as decoration. Paving stones are also usually safe.

But under supervision a reasonable result may be obtained in the flower garden and for a few weeks the vegetable patch will be kept in check.

As summer progresses the second major problem of a farm garden becomes apparent. As the garden requires attention so does the farm.

There is silage, possibly hay, more spraying, livestock, the countdown to harvest, finally harvest and autumn drilling.

Towards the middle or end of October there may be time to visit the garden again if you can find it. Some vegetables may still be worth harvesting and possibly edible. The weeds have had a good summer. Ah well, there is always next year.

What do they do in the holidays?

'Right, class, I'd like you all to concentrate very hard and think about what you did during your Easter holidays. Then write it down as neatly as you can. Yes, you can do a drawing as well. That would be nice.

'What are you doing Brian? Well it's not a very nice thing to do with your pencil is it? I'm sure Greg didn't like it either. Now please get on with your story. I'm sure you did something very interesting during your holiday. It must be fun living on a farm.

'You were helping your dad shovel what? Oh. Were you. I see. Yes, that must be – very interesting. I suppose someone has to do it. No, I don't think it would make such a good picture. Perhaps you could think of something else you did. You didn't do that all holiday did you. Yes, I suppose it would seem like it.'

'There, you see, that's much better. A drawing of an animal. It's a sheep, isn't it? Lying down I think. Er – what's that bit you're drawing now Brian? Ah. A lamb being born. Someone helping a lamb being born.

'What was the problem? I see – don't laugh, class, that word isn't funny. You see, Brian, I think the proper word is a breach delivery or possibly a malpresentation. Yes, I know that's a long word and in the heat of the moment not one your father would necessarily use.

'But we don't want to use that other word in class do we? No, we don't. Because it's not a nice word. Because I'm telling you, that's why.

'Don't start crying Diana. I'm not shouting at you. I'm not really shouting at all. Just explaining to Brian what we can and can't say in class. Or anywhere else for that matter. Those daffodils look very good, Diana.

'Yes Malcolm, if you must. No, Michael, one at a time is enough. Yes, Debbie you can say you went to visit your auntie and she wasn't in, if you really want to, but I think something which happened would be more interesting. Well, I'm sorry you had such a boring holiday.

'Now, Brian, how are we getting on with our new drawing? Oh yes, that's much better. Is it a bull? No, of course, I can see it's a cow now that you point that bit out to me although udder is the world you should really use. Please don't snigger Jonathan.

'But you are going to draw a bull as well? That will be nice. He's a Charlie is he, that's a good name for a bull, much better than Barney or Ferdinand. Oh, a Charolais. I see. And he's quite big, is he?

'All right, Greg, Brian was only repeating what the vet said about the bull's size when it stood on his foot. I don't think the vet should have said that Brian even if he was provoked and please don't say it again. Carry on with your drawing, though and get the colours right. Yes, Lindy, coming.

'Ah, Brian, you're finished. Let me see. This looks very interesting doesn't it? It's not often we see a bull standing on his hind legs, is it? Why is he doing that Brian? He's what? – please don't, Malcolm – oh yes, so he is? What a graphic picture. I'm sorry, I seem to have torn it into ten pieces and dropped it in the bucket, but don't worry I'm sure you'll soon draw another one.

'Draw daffodils this time please, or grass. A large field of green grass with nothing in it would be nice. No, nothing in it at all. Nothing stirring, not even a mouse. There is a lot of activity in the countryside but I'm beginning to think I can do without it.'

Getting your starter for ten

A friend of mine was on Mastermind.

I don't mean to slip that in as an indication that most of my friends could appear on Mastermind if they felt like it, but to explain what happened to him.

He did very well, with 17 out of 17 on his speciality subject Campbell-Bannerman. He was also going well on general knowledge until Magnus asked him the pen-name of William Connor.

Several thousand times out of several thousand he would have answered: Cassandra, the *Daily Mirror* columnist. At least he would if asked at a party, in the office, on the street or hanging by his fingertips from a cliff top.

But it may well be true that the human brain starts functioning as soon as you are born and stops only when you are asked a question in a quiz show. My friend said pass, and spent the rest of the week kicking himself as well as coming second by only two points.

I remember something similar happening to a teacher from Berwick who was also doing well until asked a question to which the answer was Berwickshire. She, too, passed and lost.

I didn't laugh at or criticise her either. Far away from the television lights, the black chair and Magnus talking rapidly, I dropped my own quiz clanger. Or something.

I think it was at Tritlington, or it may have been Cambo or Alnwick. It was certainly one of those interchangeable halls where young farmers' clubs used to hold meetings, and probably still do. I was about 16; old enough to know better. The occasion was an inter-club quiz.

The trip down had been uncomfortable enough as it was with the travelling reserve to the team of four only

moderately pleased with his position. He felt he should be in and one of us four definitely out.

He asked difficult questions all the way down from a notebook he'd compiled with the aid of Farmers' Weekly and Moore and Watson's farming bible. These questions were supposed to be toning us up, but in fact, were aimed at shredding our confidence to the point where one of us would jump out of the car screaming and leave him to it.

None of us did and our reserve settled down grumpily with the rest of the audience which, as Sod's Law would have it, was quite a big one. There must have been little else on in Tritlington, Cambo or Alnwick that night.

I started nervously, but picked up a little confidence as we went on. Only two questions stick in my mind now, one I got right and the one I got wrong.

The one I got right was the obligatory trick question, at least trick by our standard at that time – a white faced breed of Border cattle. While the rest were ransacking the Border from Berwick to Carlisle, I thought of Hereford on the Welsh border and basked in some muted applause and one call of 'Go on yersel.'

It was fairly close as we came to the final stages. The tension had risen to a fever of apathy and our reserve had finally stopped muttering to anyone who would listen.

My question was: What is a male duck? The quizmaster's mouth was already forming the word 'Correct' and the scorer was noting down one more point for Berwick when I heard myself saying: 'Gander.'

Talk about laugh. I thought our reserve would hurt himself seriously before I had the chance to choke him; the audience had been galvanised into hysterics; the scorer had snapped her pencil; the quiz-master was clenching his teeth tightly on his rolled-up question list while tears rolled down his face.

It was the most animated quiz I was ever at. Being one of the worst sports I know, but desperate not to show it, I sat there with a fixed grin until the noise died down, opening my mouth occasionally to spit out fragments of powdered teeth.

Our reserve had to be carried out semi-conscious with a suspected blood clot when he finally fell off his chair and things gradually got back to normal. I answered my last question whatever it was, successfully, but we lost by a point or two.

Several people burst out quacking when the closing ceremonies were carried out. Nobody said much in the car going home, except the reserve who had unfortunately recovered.

'Drat my duck,' he said, 'or should it be gander.'

But they had put me in the front seat for his protection, so I sat silently and gazed ahead. I still don't know why I said gander instead of drake; but it does make me very tolerant of people who make mistakes on quiz shows.

A love of wildlife is
asking for trouble

The badgers are back. At least I expect there are more than one if the size of hole and amount of soil they have excavated is anything to go by.

If there is only one, it is a grafter because we estimated the heap of soil round the mouth of the sett as about a tonne. The fact that I only guess at numbers implies, rightly, that I have yet to see a badger in the area; we see only the results of their activity.

The sett is at the base of an elm tree and the badgers seem to come and go at intervals, sometimes of months, although we try to give the tree a reasonable berth when working with tractors and implements.

Apart from the soil, the clearest evidence comes at harvest time. Freshly cut straw is cleared in patches near the sett and taken underground with stale bedding brought out.

One interesting thing we did find out was how far the burrow extends underground. A ferret on a line and fitted with a 'bleeper' was sent down at a time when the sett appeared to be empty. Donald tracked it across the field with the homing device for more than 60 yards before it turned back.

That seems a long way, although with the kind of shovels a badger has as front paws it may be a mere side street. Sometimes I think I should make the effort to sit there and wait for a badger to show itself. Then I think that as long as they are there and obviously thriving I'll let them get on with it in peace.

This is the time of year which encourages thoughts of rushing out at dawn with binoculars and camera to see what the wildlife is doing. For farmers, from a purely selfish point of view, this exercise is not as much fun as it can be for others because the wildlife is usually eating our crops.

Burns, as usual, had something to say about it when he suggested that
'A daimen icker in a thrave, 'S a sma' request' – for the mouse to make, or one ear of corn per 24 sheaves.

One mouse, one rabbit, one pigeon, would be fine. I could put up with that. The problem is their several hundred, or thousand, relatives.

Badgers don't seem to do much damage to crops except occasionally make a footpath through them. Deer, from a neighbouring small estate with parkland, used to eat a few turnips when we grew them and sometimes make a bed in a grain crop.

It's almost worth it to watch them flying along, taking fences and gates in their stride, white tails bobbing. It is also a question of numbers, because there are usually only two or three deer.

There are hundreds of rabbits and they are intensive grazers. No doubt it is because they are so common that they are unpopular. A handful of rabbits on a farm would be as welcome as the badgers and the few square yards of barley they ate would not be grudged.

But being wild rabbits a handful soon becomes a hedgeful and a few square yards becomes a few acres. The mood changes from tolerant amusement at rabbit antics to a determination to clear them out before they eat the field.

I speak from experience because we have a family of rabbits at present under the henhouse. Two or three young ones are now hopping out on to the back green, sniffing about and nibbling grass.

It fascinates the children and I'm half taken in myself. Any young animal has charm, even the young of sheep and rabbits. But we can't have a nucleus rabbit colony on the back doorstep when we're trying to eradicate them from the fields.

Angus's terrier will probably be the answer. It is starting to take a keen interest in the henhouse surrounds. I only

31

hope it is the rabbits because a hen disappeared in mysterious circumstances.

Like some ewes, this particular hen was difficult to keep in the run. It flew out once too often last week and all I found were a few handfuls of feathers. To show that nothing is wasted in nature, the sparrows had cleared all these feathers within an hour as part of their nest-building programme.

I sometimes think that the idiosyncrasies of so-called domesticated livestock are enough for one mind to cope with. Taking too much of an interest in the wildlife of a farm may be asking for trouble.

Year of the stone 'mountain'

We seem to be heading for a record crop of stones this year. Quality is rather uneven, but tonnage per acre rolled is exceptional.

I'm not sure what the reason is for this outstanding output. It could be the mild wet winter, which is getting the blame for most things.

It could be the ploughing. For various reasons, several fields were ploughed at unusual angles.

As I bend and stretch my way along tramline after tramline I wonder if stones which have slipped by the plough for years have been taken by surprise and hauled to the top like reluctant salmon.

Apart from my own modest efforts, the main reason could be Alan's conscientious rolling and the dump box on the tractor which makes stone-carrying easier.

He made a fair job of the autumn rolling we did manage to do, but has excelled himself in the spring. Occasionally, he manages a clear run from one end of the field to the other but usually stops several times to lift stones.

Net results are that we have a rising mountain range of field stones alongside a stretch of farm track which has developed into a water-logged Grand Canyon over the winter, and that Alan is superbly fit. Extremely tired, but superbly fit.

The canyon will be filled with field stones, topped off by smashed-up rubble and gravel. This will be a one day job, as in 'one day we'll get that track filled in.' We hope to get it done this summer.

At the present rate there are several more loads of stones to collect, with about 90 acres of spring barley still to roll and stones already lying in heaps in hedge backs to lift.

Despite Alan's obvious talent for the job, we decided it was unfair to put him into the aptly-named Quarry Field without some preliminary clearing. This took the best part of two days and produced four loads which creaked out of the gate-way on flattened tyres.

It wasn't unbelievable because this field is always a killer, but it was worse than usual.

The steep little slope at one end which is mainly sandstone outcrop, last remnant of the original quarry, was thickly strewn. Here and there young barley shoots peeped through, but my part-time helper and I talked in whispers in case we started an avalanche.

It was like picking potatoes, only harder on the hands. As long as you could judge distance correctly there was no need to straighten up – simply flick the stones onto the trailer and inch forward to the next two.

There were exceptions. One had to be put on the loader, and several had to be beaten with a hammer into several pieces of manageable size.

From the diagonal, rather sandy strip which, until filled in, used to be a Municipal Amenity Compound – for 30 years until they put that sign up it had been a rubbish tip or coup – we lifted the usual load of lumber.

Plastic squeezy bottles and empty paste jars are the most persistent rubbish, but the lumps of old metal can do most damage to combines. There is also one patch which produces half a load of old tarmac each year.

Once through that, things improved. There was only the stiff clay slope to produce a fine sample of small boulders and the usual range of stones across the rest of the field.

The secret of lifting stones, either when rolling or walking behind a trailer, is to pace yourself. The tendency with both methods is to start the day at a gallop by lifting everything much bigger than a marble.

During a long day this enthusiasm can be replaced by a feeling akin to exasperation. You either throw stones into trailer of dump box in a tired frenzy, or try to ignore everything except those which stick out like Ayre's Rock on the Australian desert.

34

It is a job which has to be approached in a spirit of calm determination. How long we can keep this up I don't know; the sooner more spraying becomes urgent the better.

The bank that likes to say . . .

The scene: a bank manager's office somewhere in Scotland –
'Well, well, nice to see you again. Please come in.'
'Well, I can't say it's all that grand to be here. I'm not sure what it's all about?'
'Well, I'll be frank with you. Head office did have just one or two queries about your cash flow for this year.'
'Aye?'
'Aye – I mean yes.'
'Well?'
'Well what?'
'Well – what are the queries. I thought I'd given you all the information you needed.'
'Not . . . not quite, I think. There were just one or two things, small things you understand, that didn't . . . didn't quite fit.'
'Such as?'
'Now I don't want you to take this the wrong way – but we think your anticipated wheat yields might be slightly on the high side. Slightly, you understand.'
'How slightly?'
'Oh – about a tonne. I mean, I really think four tonnes an acre is a bit high. And your price seems rather optimistic at £135 a tonne.'
'But that's what I need next September to make the books balance.'
'That's right – on the rest of your figures, that is what you need. But the point is I – that is, head office, – don't think you'll get it.'
'Peter Hepworth gets it. Oliver Walston gets it.'
'And so they should. But I'm not their banker. I am your banker. And on the basis of past performance, you're not

36

going to get four tonnes an acre. And nobody's going to get
£135 a tonne . . .'
'Milling – it's going for milling, man.'
'But you don't know that. And even if it did you wouldn't get
the yield to go with it. Furthermore, you've never managed
to get it accepted for milling before.'
'There always a first time. My crop consultant says the
wheats are looking well . . .'
'Your what!'
'Crop consultant. Nice lad, charges only £5 an acre. Says
he'll get my yields up where they should be PDQ.'
'PD what?'
'Don't know – think it's a new spray.'
'Well that explains one outstanding item on the cash flow
anyway. We'll take that off.'
'Now look . . .'
'No, I'm afraid you'll have to look. Expenditure has to be
trimmed to the bone. For instance, what's this new tractor
doing here?'
'I always buy a new tractor every second year.'
'You're not listening, are you – you can't afford it. There is
not enough money. The money is not there. On the most
optimistic assessment the money will not be there at harvest
time either. You cannot afford new machinery . . ."
'But I need a new tractor.'
'You don't – the ones you've got are fine. They'll last for
years.'
'I've always had a new tractor. The lambs'll pay for it . . .'
'Ah. That's another thing. At a rough estimate, your
lambing percentage will have to be 258 and they'll have to
average £52 through June to August to give the returns
you're talking about.'
'Yes?'
'Drat it, the best you've ever done is 165 per cent and if they
average £40 in July and August you'll be doing well.'
'I've changed the tups this year.'
'I don't believe I'm hearing this. I see your lips moving, but I
can't believe you're saying these things. You're not on drugs
or anything are you?'

37

'Just a shot of pulpy kidney vaccine the other day – nothing to worry about. Look, I think you're being rather hard on me.'

'It's for your own good. There's absolutely no point in trying to work from these figures. You're in cloud cuckoo land. I mean look at them – malting barley, £150 a tonne at 56cwt an acre . . . oilseed, 36cwt at £380 a tonne . . .'

'They say there's going to be a shortage . . .'

'Rent to come down by 25 per cent . . . diesel prices expected to drop 30 pence a gallon . . . buy fertiliser early and get £35 a tonne off . . .'

'It might . . .'

'Look – a cash flow has to assume the worst. You have to expect all costs to rise and all returns to be low. And the bank has to know what your cropping and stock figures are at the beginning and end to make it mean anything. Now, quite frankly, I've worked out my own cash flow for you and the conclusion is clear – there is no money left . . .'

'Right then, well I'll be getting back . . .'

'Did you hear what I said? There is no money. You have no money. The money is not there.'

'Fine, that's grand then, thanks for your help . . .'

'Excuse me – watch my lips. You are, or very soon will be, broke – bust – skint – bankrupt – penniless.'

'I see – is this bad? Will it affect my tax position next year. And does it mean I don't get an increase in the overdraft?'

'Correct. You may not even get an overdraft at all.'

'Well, this is a fine thing after all I've done for you. A fine thing.'

'Sorry, dad, but you wanted me to be a bank manager.'

Waking up to reality

When the sun rises before five on a misty, dew soaked world, my thoughts turn lightly to milking cows. And I reflect happily on the fact that I am pleased not to be doing it.

Milking cows for a living was always well down the list of things I wanted to do and for most of my life I've succeeded in keeping it there. But writing about some of the technical aspects of dairy farming last week brought many of the practical problems back to me.

It was a long time ago, half a lifetime in fact, at this time of year. That was a benefit. No struggling about in the dark or spending the day mucking out byres and carting straw between milkings.

On reflection, I had it easy. A May, June and July of fairly good weather, cows out at grass and even at five in the morning the sun was beginning to shine.

I could have been doing many worse things than striding through wet grass chivvying up cows. Given half a chance I would have been, but it was a three-month sentence without remission. So I made the best of it and got to quite like that time in the morning.

In fact, like most people who have to get up early out of necessity I made a virtue out of it. I went round like that worst of all pests, a converted smoker, saying how wonderful it was to be up and about for the dawn chorus.

Much of this chorus was actually drowned out by me bawling at the meandering cows. I can see them now, slow and Ayrshire, trundling across the field – Tibby, Fairy, Old Fairy, Dina, Spot – with bloodcurdling curses ringing round their ears.

It would be nice to say they responded. They didn't. Their speed towards the gate never varied by more than a fraction whether I bawled myself blue in the face or idled behind watching the sunrise.

There are advantages in getting up early, particularly in the summer. Not many clothes are required and it is possible to put on shirt, jeans and wellingtons while asleep and walking downstairs.

I was reminded of the wisdom of A. G. Street's father, who regularly lay in bed until nine o'clock, a stay which included his breakfast and the morning mail.

This scandalised his neighbours and friends who liked to convince the world and themselves that they were out and about at first light. They gave Mr Street senior a lot of cheek to the effect that he was letting the side down.

He replied:

'At least when I get up, I'm awake.'

As I trotted downstairs in the mornings, I wished I could say the same thing. Luckily, I waken up quickly in fresh air. Going to bed before one o'clock most mornings would have helped too.

Apart from bringing in the cows, the actual milking was also pleasant enough, starting with a bucket of cold water and a cloth to wash down udders. I always considered what effect this treatment would have had on me, but the cows didn't seem to mind.

Then there was the real business of slipping teat cups, in clusters of four, on and off and carrying full stainless-steel

40

buckets to the dairy and the cooler. Filling the churns and manhandling them to the cart came later.

Afterwards there was hosing down and brushing out the passage and gutters, with the herd safely at grass, having travelled back in the same unhurried way they came in.

But never at any time did I think of making a career of it. Dairy farming friends say, lips curling, that the reason is quite obvious – to be dedicated, hard-working, prepared for the seven-day week, twelve-months a year slog.

The correct reply to this is to invite them to rearrange two words into a well-known phrase or saying which has little to do with dairy farming.

Deep down, however, I think they may be right. Twice daily feeding of pigs, calves or cattle may be just as routine and tying as twice-daily milking, but there does not seem to be the same inevitability about it.

There were breaks on the dairy farm. Occasionally I dozed on the couch. Or, with spectacular results, I dozed on the steerage hoe; the aim of this job is to clear all weeds between rows of turnips, not leave neat rows of weeds and yards of slaughtered turnips as my eyes closed in the sunshine.

Alfie, my employer, was only moderately pleased about this, although kind. Similar haphazard results when turning hay, which I tried to blame on tiredness, he was inclined to dismiss as insanity. I started going to bed earlier.

Things improved and I became half-proficient with cows. But even then, and allowing for the diversions such as steerage hoeing. I felt that I was milking 24 hours a day. Since then, I've confined my dairying to theory.

Just occasionally, at this time of year on a fine, sunny morning I think briefly about milking cows. But not for long.

I get a kick out of ewe

I met a man the other day who was nursing a swollen wrist which seemed painful. He agreed that it was.

'Damn ewe,' he said in an injured tone. 'I was going to give her a smack on the nose and she moved her head. I'm still not sure if it's broken.'

When I asked if he meant the ewe's head he muttered something under his breath and went away still shielding his arm and wincing.

Our brief conversation gave an insight into the way we view our livestock. He didn't see it as his own fault for trying to hit the ewe in the first place, but as her fault because she took avoiding action.

I felt the same way when I took a well-meaning kick at a bullock and connected with a metal post instead. Lying there wondering whether to take the wellington off or drive to the hospital with it on I realised I had made a mistake.

Not in trying to kick the bullock, which was on its fifth circuit of the pen we were trying to move it from when I missed, but in being too close to the trough at the time.

There may be those who think that the man driven to violence by the ewe, and I, deserved all we got for mistreating animals. I can only say that there was no sadistic or brutal intention involved.

We hadn't set out with the idea of picking on an animal and giving it a systematic beating. All we had tried to do, as with a disobedient child, had been to show them the error of their ways.

Anyone who has kept livestock has done something similar, I suspect. Those who say they haven't can be put in the same category as those couples celebrating 50 years of marriage with never an argument or cross word to look back on.

That is, they are remarkable and saintly people or have very short memories. I think the latter more likely, a thought which came to me when we were weaning pigs which had been running with their mothers in straw yards.

This method of keeping pigs is low on cost, but can be high on irritability – mine, not the pigs'.

The problem is that six-week-old pigs, weighing 10 to 12 kilos, can move quickly, often in several directions at the same time. Knowing this, and also how patient I can be when moving livestock, I have perfected my theory that the only way to move pigs is very quietly.

This theory is fine. It is the practice that causes problems as my good resolutions crumble with every small pig which breaks back towards mother or squeezes through some hole I thought was securely blocked.

In fact, we usually manage without too much fuss, walking the sows out at one side before penning the small pigs ready to collect with the trailer. But it can go wrong and once on the loose among nooks, crannies and dunging areas, small, lively, agitated pigs take a lot of cornering by large, lively, agitated pigmen.

There is something about it which brings out the worst in people, notably when the last one to be caught insists on it being done in the dirtiest corner while squealing loudly – the pig, that is, not the pigman, although by that stage there may not be much to choose between them.

Loading porkers for the mart can also be interesting. Often they trot quietly along the loading alley and into the truck; just occasionally they refuse to move at all and it is this unpredictability which keeps a loader on his toes. When they do refuse to move and have to be carried aboard, it is clear where the expression 'pig-headed' comes from. There is no point in hitting a pig which is determined not to move; it may make a tempting target but any satisfaction is purely temporary.

That is even more true with cattle. A porker can at least be restrained by a gate or hurdle and gradually forced to go where you want it to go, but half a ton of bull or bullock is a different proposition if it turns round and charges back.

Most can be deterred by facing up to them, but now and again they run straight on. There is nothing to be gained by hitting it as it goes past, strong though the temptation may be; patience and kindness is the only answer and if you believe that you'll believe anything.

Hard jobs for the lads

A striking feature of much farm work now is that most of it is done by individuals working alone, or at least isolated from each other in their tractors or combines.

It is unusual to get people working in pairs whereas at one time pairs, threes and even quartets were the rule rather than the exception, although wise employers made an exception with 'laddies'.

The rule of thumb for youngsters was that one lad on his own might get quite a lot of work done, two lads would do about half that amount and three lads would do no work at all.

It is now rare to find farms employing more than one lad at a time and the adult labour force continues to shrink. There simply aren't so many people, employed or family, on the farms.

We have become capital intensive rather than labour extensive with much money tied up in bigger, labour saving machinery and equipment. I sometimes think that more people and less machinery would be a good thing, but the stumbling block is what you would expect these extra people to do; more important, what would they be prepared to do.?

We have come too far along the road of mechanisation and automation now. When youngsters want jobs, as several million of them do, the don't mean that they want the kind of dirty, heavy drudgery associated with so much hand labour on farms in the past.

Weeks on end spent mucking out with graips, all grain handled in sacks, crops weeded by hand, the chaff house and the turnip cutter, turnip baskets and bucket feeding.

Come to think of it, some things haven't changed much after all, but there is a difference between doing it for yourself and being paid a pittance to do it for someone else.

Some of the communal jobs such as haymaking and harvest could be enjoyable, and there was a time when I quite liked singling turnips or sugar beet. But generally speaking I came in at the end of labour-intensive farming and have to say that there are many jobs I don't miss.

Handling grain in sacks is one. When I pick up a hundredweight bag of grain now I find it hard to believe that until the 1960s barley was in two-cwt sacks and wheat in 18-stone sacks. Wheeling them on a sack-barrow was all right, but carrying them was something else.

Just to clarify the terminology for those who have been metricated, seed grain now comes in 50 kilo paper bags. Barley going off the farm used to go in what would have been 102 kilo hessian sacks if kilos had been in use; wheat was handled in 115 kilo sacks.

Lifting them was a matter of pride, even carrying them upstairs at the risk of a hernia after they had been lowered on to your back. But doubling them or even, perish the thought,

trebling them when floor space was running out was the real test.

It was usually done by two men working in tandem. The technique was for each to take a top corner of the bag with one hand and slide a short, stout stick under the bottom of the bag, held between you. Then lift while grunting.

A keen youngster simply holds his end of the stick and gets ready to lift. A veteran lifter, a split second before the lift begins, suddenly yanks as much stick to his side as possible.

By some law – gravity, relativity, thermodynamics or simple physics – this ploy throws most of the weight onto the keen youngster. He doesn't like to admit defeat and heaves away gamely in imminent danger of a seizure until the bag is in place and the veteran grunts in sympathy.

As a keen youngster I looked forward to being a veteran and practising the technique on someone else. But first sacks became smaller, by law, and before long all grain was being handled in bulk.

Machinery replaced men, hardly surprising when you think that the most powerful of human beings can muster just about as much strength as a one-third horsepower electric motor.

There are still dirty and heavy jobs on the farm, but not nearly as many as there used to be. We should all be glad about that. I still think there is a place for more people on farms, but not by a return to hard labour.

First, catch your gimmer

Well now, here we are reporting for Out and About in the Country and this week we are covering an instruction day for sheep shearers.

This is the time of year when sheep have to lose their wool otherwise they get too hot, sticky and uncomfortable and have, I'm told, one more excuse for dropping dead.

I'm also told that as soon as the sheep are sheared the weather changes and half of them get pneumonia. Some shepherds call this time of the year yowe-tremble.

But that doesn't seem to worry this bunch of cheery lads who are here to learn how to do it and, believe me, it's not as easy as it looks.

Well, the instructor's giving them a few words of welcome and advising them on their equipment. Now here's the first part – he's showing them how to fit the cutter and comb to their electric shears.

Ah – there's a lad with a slight problem. The instructor is asking politely how far he intends to get with the cutter on upside down. What a nice smile the instructor has.

Right, says the instructor, here's the basic style. First catch your ewe. He's asking one of the trainees to step into the catching pen and bring one out. He's in, he's got one – no, he hasn't – yes, he has – he hasn't – he has – he's down – he's up – he's under – here he comes – there he goes.

Ah well, I suppose falling off was the best thing he could have done in the circumstances. They've managed to catch that ewe at last – my, she's a lively one. The instructor thinks she's sweating too much to use as an example, so he's put her back in the pen and brought out another one.

Yes, she's much smaller and looks much more docile. Very docile indeed. She's lying very quietly as the instructor demonstrates the basic style – feet this way, that way, broad sweeps of the shears, roll her round with the knees, grip firmly, but not too tight. She certainly is a quiet ewe.

Now a final flourish and the instructor stands up while the ewe gets up and trots o . . . no, she's not moving at all. No, even that yank on the ear hasn't moved her – I don't think the kiss of life seems to be working either . . .

The instructor seems to be suggesting that this is the first time this unlikely occurrence has happened to him. He also seems to be questioning the justice of it happening to him now in front of a bunch of laughing hyenas . . . yes, I think one of the trainees is having hysterics over there.

I must say the instructor removed the deceased very quickly and he's pressing on with the course now that they've quietened down again.

He's asking one of the most promising trainees to tackle the next one while he advises. Yes, he's got her out of the pen. I'm told she's a grand mule gimmer this one.

It looks to me, though I'm not an expert, that this lad is getting on quite well. One or two small nicks in the skin, but nothing to worry about says the instructor, he's done worse things shaving. Pour a bit of oil on it and he'll get a needle and thread later.

This is the tricky bit though. Be very careful going round the . . . oh dear, he seems to have cut one off. The instructor has gone quite white under that nice tan he has – he's imploring the trainee to be careful particularly round the udder and he's pointing out where he wants him to shear . . . oh, that looked quite painful.

The instructor has gone for a sharp trot round the shed with his index finger jammed between his thighs – no, now he's sucking it and mumbling for a bandage. The ewe has just rolled onto her back and kicked the trainee upside down – two more of them have caught her and held her down – ah, someone's managed to switch the machine off.

That was really most interesting. I wonder what's next?

I've got to give this instructor full marks for perseverance – he may be bloodied, but he's unbowed. At least he was until that Suffolk tup hit him just there. He may walk with a limp for some time.

But he's going on. He's saying something about being good and mad now. He's caught one with horns – now, I don't know much about this, but that may not be a wise choice at this stage. Ah, I feared as much – I thought those horns looked tricky. Handy for swinging her round your head of course – well caught, lad.

That seems to be it. Most interesting. I'll just ask the instructor how he enjoyed his day . . . on second thoughts, we'll just make our excuses and, Bye till next time.

The age of designer farms?

Desmond Bucket was discontented. It wasn't simply the fact that one of his unsociable neighbours had shouted at him that morning as he, Desmond, did a handbrake turn followed by a 'wheelie' while picking up the papers.

'What's the difference between a Range Rover and a hedgehog then,' the man had bawled at him in a fury, driving off in a muddy tractor before Desmond could catch the reply.

Strange people, he thought. Couldn't get through to them at all and he'd been here for nearly three years. When he had been stockbroking – or was it merchant banking? – before he had decided to renovate the countryside, he got to know people very quickly.

Why, he'd known some of his best friends less than a year when he had decided to move to the heart of rural Britain and show them how it should be done.

The few million from the family had helped of course, given with the instruction that he had to keep farming until it was all gone, ha ha.

Uncle George had once attended a dinner in the Farmers' Club in London and always remembered that joke about the farmer who won the pools and was asked what he would do with the fortune: 'Well, I'll just keep farming away until it's all gone.'

It was true, Desmond concluded, that returns from farming were not as good as those from stockbroking – or was it merchant banking? In fact they weren't really as good as those for being a busker on the London underground.

To be honest, his losses so far had been astonishing and it was just as well the several million had been there to begin with. Reforming the countryside was not so easy as it seemed and he was saddened and disappointed with the way land prices had collapsed since he bought his farms.

Originally he thought one farm might do, but with several people apparently keen to sell at once he thought he might as well do the thing properly. Strange, they had all been friendly enough then.

Getting his priorities right had been the next thing. The house had cost rather more than expected to redesign and restructure as a slightly smaller version of Alnwick Castle and the swimming pool smelt faintly of sheep dip when the wind was in the east.

But the bounce was true on the tennis court and the new steading had won a design award. True it got a little messy when livestock were actually in the buildings, but the man employed full time with the rotary brush took care of that.

The drier was a thing of beauty, reminding everyone of a rocket on the launching pad at Cape Canaveral and costing approximately as much. The salesman who had sold that deal to him was now living permanently in the Channel Isles, he'd heard; you wouldn't think there would be much demand for farm machinery in Alderney.

Trees, 'Our only renewable resource,' had been planted in

large numbers on specially chosen sites and that had won a conservation award. Hand made wooden gates rather than those ugly tubular steel efforts were on every field and had won a Preserve Rural Britain commendation.

Livestock were only the best, pedigree where possible and expensive whether pedigree or not.

Whenever he bought stock at the mart he could hear farmers murmur to each other and was occasionally close enough to hear one say to another:
'Well they certainly saw him coming,' and he knew they already respected his acumen.

Strangely, the stock never seemed to look as well when he got them home and those he sold again never made anything like as much as he had paid. He put this down to mineral deficiency and spent many thousands on trace elements and feed blocks.

A year seemed quite long enough to establish himself as a pedigree breeder of note so large signs went up on all roads leading to the farms. Publicity must be a good idea, he thought, and was rather hurt when he found several of the signs blasted like a collander by some lunatic with a shotgun.

No, Desmond sighed, leaning on a gate as he had seen a farmer do in a film and wondering why his wheat had not done the 4½ tons an acre promised by the firm of management consultants, the rural life wasn't all it was cracked up to be.

He couldn't actually bring himself to invite a few of them round. Sometimes he thought he would like to, but he was afraid of the conversation turning to enzootic abortion and difficult calvings at the dinner table.

He would just have to keep on spending away until they realised how good a farmer he was and the dramatic effect a few more like him could have on the countryside.

What was the difference between a hedgehog and a Range Rover anyway?

A sense of past glories

It used to be the fashion in stately homes and castles – and possibly still is because my acquaintance with them is limited – to decorate the walls with the heads and hides of big game.

Beneath the glassy stares of the deceased lions, tigers, water buffalo, elk, okapi and boar the proud owner could explain how he came by them.

It struck me that in these parlous times when farmers are being urged to diversify to survive and also communicate with the public that there is an opportunity here. Our homes may not be stately except for isolated pockets of plutocracy, but they could certainly be made interesting. I take an example, hypothetical of course:

'Right then ladies and gentlemen, we're at what is known as the back door. Note the large and varied assortment of footwear, some qualifying as antique. Yes, you may take photographs.

Don't . . . ah well, never mind. I was going to say it's not advisable to lift a wellington except by gloved hand and definitely not advisable to hold one upside down to study the lack of tread.

What you have just tipped on the floor is approximately 2½lb of barley from the 1986 harvest. But don't worry. It's less trouble to sweep up than oilseed rape.

The distinctive aroma you can detect – don't all fight to get through the door at once please, there's an old lady down there being trampled – is silage. Not one of the great silages, I would say, but with a certain bouquet to it.

I had hoped to spend rather longer at the back door. There was quite an interesting selection of sticks, syringes, aerosols and empty penicillin bottles I would like to have drawn your attention to, but as we're in the kitchen we may as well go on.

The centrepiece of the kitchen – yes, well apart from Willie, who was up all night with a difficult calving and says he isn't going to put a shirt on to have his breakfast for anybody – is the cooker.

Yes, right, you've all seen a cooker before, only trying to spin it out a little. I agree Willie isn't a pretty sight. We may try to have him shaved and embalmed before the next party comes through. I think you will find the dining room interesting – it's an idea we borrowed from Alnwick castle.

Don't handle the exhibits please, I've had enough trouble getting the screws to stay in the wall as it is. The bull's head has been on the floor twice this morning already.

I knew you'd be interested. Now this first one here on my left, pet lamb, circa 1987. Death due to natural causes – well, natural to a pet lamb that is, hung itself in the rubber tube on the Save That Lamb colustrum syringe.

Next, the hide of a Continental cross heifer of a breed which shall be nameless but which we'll call Limousin to protect the innocent. A flight pattern of 398 yards, that is you came in the gate at one side of the field and she jumped the fence at the other.

Brought down at 600 yards by a Bisley marksman while heading for the Tyne Tunnel. Skinned on the spot by a demented herdsman, who is fortunately now recovering and can be visited on alternate Wednesdays provided he's had his injection.

Ah, one of my favourites. The salesman who bought our malting barley at a £20 premium then contra accounted what we owed for fertiliser before rejecting the barley for high nitrogen.

Just a joke there. It's only a mask, but the devious expression is extremely realistic.

Here we have the boar which reduced a pig trailer to matchwood when being loaded then chewed an aluminium shovel down to the hand-grip which I happened to be holding while clinging with my other hand to a rafter.

We finally loaded him with the forklift bucket and asked for the head and tusks as a memento. Was he wild? Well, he wasn't very pleased.

One or two minor exhibits there – skin and fleece of a mule ewe, a collie's ear, a farmyard cat, turkey's feet.

And here we are in the living room with various items of farming memorabilia – a smashed moisture meter from the 1985 harvest, an autographed photo of Michael Jopling – yes, the one with dart holes in it – Highly Commended ticket for the mule gimmer class in 1965, a final final demand from the water board, smashed rain gauge from July 1987 and many more.

Browse through, take your time, work your way to the front porch, admire the natural wilderness of the front garden which should please the conservationists and nature lovers among you.

And don't forget an offering in the poor box as you go out – that's it, the one marked Bank. Have a nice day.'

Dung not a lyrical subject

There is a passage in the novel *Sunset Song* where the farmer Ewan Tavendale, serving at the front during the First World War, is to be shot for desertion.

As he talks to a friend in the final hours, what he remembers most keenly is the smell of cattle dung being spread on his parks of an April morning.

It might seem an odd quirk of memory, or in this case the novelist Gibbon's imagination, but anyone who has handled dung could understand how it might happen.

Cattle dung may not be a subject to get lyrical about and I suspect any poetry on it would only be found on walls, but as dung goes it is probably the best choice if one has to be made.

Without going too deeply into it (Freudian slip one), in a varied career I have handled (slip two) most types.

Cat and dog are unpleasant. Emptying cesspits yourself is one way of widening your circle of friends and colleagues rapidly.

Emptying them with a specialist tanker driver is an education, as is inspecting these rural necessities with the local council troubleshooter.

I have seldom seen a man so enthusiastic about his work. My approach to cesspit manhole covers is to lift them gingerly in some trepidation.

The specialist came equipped with his iron hooks with which he lifted heavy metal covers in seconds and gazed with delight on the pleasures within.

'That,' he said in the voice of a connoisseur who has just found a fine example of porcelain, 'is a lovely crust down there.'

He picked up a stick and poked the contents about gently. 'Lovely,' he said again. 'That means the bacteria are really working well.'

He put the stick down regretfully. 'You don't get a crust like that very often these days. All these detergents and germ killers going down the sink.'

Lovely crust or not, we had three cesspits which were due to be emptied and one pipe unblocked. It was the side effects of this blockage which had persuaded me to get the council expert's opinion.

As in the past, his advice was correct. The colloquial expression for being knowledgeable or skilful has never been more apt than in his case.

Which brought us to the visit from the tanker driver, in the job for 22 years. With powerful suction pumps, lengths of piping, rubber gloves, and wellingtons it is not a dirty job as such; it is not one I could see myself sticking at for 22 days never mind 22 years.

He seemed to enjoy it. There was many a merry quip as I showed him round and lent a hand with as much enthusiasm as I could generate.

When we had finished I went back to mucking out cattle courts with some relief. I left him eating his sandwiches before moving on to the next pool of delights.

To disagree marginally with the late Grassic Gibbon, dung when spread has an evocative smell. But I prefer the

fresh biting smell of dung being ripped out of the courts onto trailers in JCB-fork size chunks.

It is a job where you have the feeling of getting somewhere. The shed empties, and the midden grows. The sharp smell of fresh dung is in the air where it is fine. But when the smell accumulates indoors the room begins to seem a little crowded. As when handling chemicals or silage, it is better to remove all outer garments completely and only to venture indoors if absolutely necessary before the end of the day.

Looking on the sheepish side in the judging ring

I don't know what I'd expected – possibly a bigger crowd round the ringside for the biggest sheep section at the Highland Show, possibly a few words of encouragement for my first judging stint.

It wasn't like that at all. Under a typical lowering Highland Show sky two stewards marched me briskly into the ring as a wave of apathy swept over the pundits, leaning on the rails.

It's a big moment for a first-time judge, particularly someone not directly involved with the breed. I tried hard to remember what I had to look for as the first class walked proudly into the ring. It was like a bad dream as they kept coming. I'd thought perhaps a first class of half a dozen entries would give me a start, a chance to order my thoughts.

A grand head, that was one thing I had to look for. Now there was a grand head over there, just enough bone in the right places, good marking, sound teeth. Pity it belonged to the shepherd, but you can't have everything: I mentally marked him down as a first prizewinner if nothing better showed up. By now there were about 30 sheep in the ring with their exhibitors.

'Biggest class we've ever had,' the steward whispered proudly.

'Take an hour to place this one, it'll build up the suspense and drive them crazy in the press room wondering what's happened to the result.'

'An hour!' I screamed in a whisper. 'The audience'll lynch me if I footer about here for an hour on 30 entries. If I was drawing this lot at home – and I've got better ones there, I'll tell you – I'd have them sorted out in 10 minutes.'

That was for the stewards' benefit. For the life of me I couldn't think why I'd accepted the invitation in the first place. It was like a nightmare. The sheep seemed identical and I hadn't seen one showing wonderful breed character yet.

However, as the main character I'd noticed about this breed was their penchant for dropping dead on slight provocation, perhaps that wasn't surprising either. I'd try prodding one to see how much was flesh and how much padded wool. I did, and it cleared the rails. I dropped it from the list of possibles.

I was sure the sky was getting darker as I walked intently up and down the row of hopeful shining faces. That young lady with the nice smile could certainly take her entry several places up the line.

And if I wasn't mistaken that was the breeder who'd given me a hard time at last year's show, prancing about for an hour with his tup until the *Scottish Farmer* photographer got it at just the right angle. I'd save them both some trouble this year – his entry could get back to the pen.

In a funny sort of way I was starting to enjoy myself. I wondered what the livestock showring did for small industries as I wiped black boot polish off one sheep's feet, patted flour and powder off another, and idly scraped wax off the horns of a third.

I realised that the rumbling noise wasn't thunder, but growls of discontent from the exhibitors and, increasingly, from the ringside. The natives were getting restless and the steward was getting anxious.

'Give them a sign that you know what you're doing,' he muttered.

'They won't believe it,' I muttered back. 'I've never seen a ringside yet that believed a judge knew what he was doing. The whole system's based on the theory that the judge will make a horlicks of it – it gives the punters something to talk about for the rest of the day.

'Even better, you should have two judges, like the Clydesdales, so that they can disagree and bring an umpire in. Try that if you find watching paint dry too exciting.'

He grimaced, or possibly whimpered. The sky was darker still and I wondered for a moment where the Gurkha pipe band had come from. They didn't seem too happy about my approach either.

It was time for decisions. Swiftly I decided on a short leet. I did this by taking every fifth entry. It didn't seem to meet universal approval, but I was past caring while the pipe band was getting louder I asked the short leet survivors to let their entries run about. One ran straight into a post and broke its neck and a further two started butting each other furiously. The six sheep grazed unconcerned.

There was only one way to decide. I took the dice from my pocket and rolled it.

The die was cast. Number four in line had won. It turned out to be a camel. The sky was pitch black. The Gurkhas had stopped piping and drawn their kukris. The steward, now with long ears and whiskers, pulled on his white gloves and disappeared down a rabbit hole.

As I crawled sweating from underneath the bedclothes I knew why I would wait a long time for an invitation to judge at the Highland Show. What I couldn't understand was where the black boot polish had come from.

Cashing in on advice

'Next. Good afternoon – Smithers isn't it?'

'Yes sir.'

'Well, that's a good start. Now tell me Smithers, what have you in mind when you leave this wonderful seat of learning?'

'Well, sir . . .'

'Don't be bashful lad. What's it to be? Merchant banker – accountant – stockbroker – company chairman's personal assistant? All good jobs, lad – just mention the name of this wonderful seat of learning and you're well in.'

'Well sir – I've been thinking . . .'

'Careful now, Smithers – don't do anything rash I always say. You're not here to learn to think.'

'Yes sir – I know – but I suppose a thought rather sneaked up on me – and I thought I'd quite like to be an agricultural consultant. Gosh, are you all right?'

'Yes, yes, fine, boy fine. I just feel rather pale, a possible heart spasm there. I thought you said something about agriculture.'

'Yes, I did.'

'But that's preposterous. Agriculture! Farming! It's all sticky and smelly and great heaps of grain and pulling out hedges and spoiling pheasant shoots isn't it? I mean – you wouldn't actually think of shovelling the stuff would you?'

'Of course not, sir. I'd be advising people with farms how to farm them.'

'But you don't know anything about farming, Smithers'

'Oh, don't worry about that sir. It hasn't stopped my brother doing pretty well. He's running 20,000 acres for a management company now – doing it frightfully well too. Knows every acre like the back of his hand – his gross margins on wheat are the talk of the Farmers' Club.'

'Spare me the technical details, Smithers. As I remember Smithers Major had trouble adding to 10 and subtraction was beyond him – and 20,000 acres does seem rather a lot. I mean an acre's very nearly the size of a rugger pitch isn't it?'

'Possibly, sir. I don't think it really matters that much as long as you've got enough of them. Not yourself personally of course – that's asking for trouble my brother says. But if you've enough to look after for someone else, that's spot on.'

'But if it's bad news to be owning all these acres why would a consultant be such a good job?'

'Oh come on, sir – I'd be getting paid a lot of money for telling them what to do. I mean if I actually farmed I'd have to make a profit, wouldn't I? Advising a farmer is quite different.'

'You're losing me here, Smithers. You're advising farmers but your brother – Lord save us – is actually farming?'

'Well, not exactly, sir. He's running this 20,000 acres for people who can't run it themselves. A bit pathetic really – most of them could make quite a reasonable living if they put their minds to it, but they think he's wonderful because of the profit he makes for them.'

'He actually makes a profit then?'

'Well, it's quite easy really. Most of it is land with no mortgage charges on it. He just flattens all the old buildings, sacks all the staff, ploughs everything out, sells all the livestock, spends a few hundred thousand on big machinery and off they go. Simple.'

'It certainly sounds like it. Why any idiot could do that.'

'Exactly, sir. That's the beauty of it. Any idiot does.'

'So you'd be well qualified, Smithers.'

'Thank you sir.'

'But, to return to my question, you'd be advising farmers and not running a million acres or whatever yourself?'

'Oh, to begin with sir. I suppose I can't take on 20,000 acres straight away. I'll join a firm of estate agents or something and get paid for advising farmers.'

'I don't suppose there's any danger of your fees being linked to . . . er . . . their profits, or anything like that?'

'Ha, ha, ha. Oh dear me no. We charge them 10 to 15

64

thousand a year for advice regardless. It's even better than stockbroking or accountancy.'

'And what sort of advice do you give them, considering you know nothing about the subject?'

'Oh, I'll probably do a year at Cirencester to get some of the technical terms nearly right. Then it's mainly a matter of telling them to flatten the old buildings, sack most of the staff, buy some big new equipment, plough everything out, sell all the livestock – pretty simple, really.'

'Smithers, you've got more nous than I gave you credit for. Good luck, though I'm sorry for your clients. Next.'

Start from scratch in our restaurant!

'I've got it. We'll open a café.'

'No, let's call it a restaurant. It'll not make any difference to what we serve.'

'Okay. Good idea. Have you any experience in catering?'

'None.'

'Good. That means we don't have have to cope with any preconceived notions. We can start from scratch.'

'Right. That's true. But I have been doing some research into what we need for a successful restaurant these days.'

'Does good cooking come into it?'

'Not as far as I could tell.'

'That's good because I can't cook. But I can use a microwave.'

'Fine. Fine. That'll cover most eventualities. But look, we'll get to that in a minute. Let's take it from the beginning. We've got the restaurant – right?'

'Right. We'll call it Not the Café Royale or The Ubiquitous Boiled Potato – or something.'

'Or something. Okay. The customer comes in, or customers . . .'

'. . . and we welcome them like long lost friends, right?'

'Wrong. Ignore them for a minute or two. Let them hang about the door, wondering if they're good enough for us. I've noticed that giving them an inferiority complex cuts out at least half the potential complaints.'

'I see. Subtle stuff. But we acknowledge them eventually?'

'Oh yes. Have to, you know. We need their money. Stroll over and look down your nose at them. Make an effort to find them a table.'

'But there might be plenty of empty tables.'
'We know that. But they don't. Say they're all booked. Make them feel glad to get a seat. Give them a menu and take a drinks order.'
'They might not want a drink.'
'Be positive. Make them feel bad if they don't want one. That's where half the profits come from, particularly if it's a family – get the kids knocking back the soft drinks.'
'Good – I'm with you. So they order a starter, soup of the day or something like that.'
'Yes – and you must know the rule about soup of the day?'
'The waiter – or waitress – never knows what it is?'
'Right. You're catching on. And the chef's special is always paté. Egg mayonnaise is mainly salad cream, and prawn cocktail is mainly shredded lettuce and that funny pink stuff.'
'So we can do a starter for about 10p.'
'Top whack I'd say. And price them at £1.20 upwards.'
'Rolls and butter on the table of course?'
'No, no, no . . . I thought you were following me. A dry roll if they ask for one. Small plastic packets of butter and those little tubs of cream for the coffee.'
'The ones that spill all over when you finally rip the tab off the top?'
'That's the ones. Keep catering plastic, I say.'
'Wouldn't it be cheaper to have a dish of butter and a jug of cream?'
'Think of the work. It's so convenient with those little plastic packs and wrappers.'
'Except for the customers.'
'We're not running things for their benefit are we? Plastic long life cream and silly little wrapped pats of butter it is, preferably imported.'
'Are we going to use any fresh food from the district – there's lots of it about at different times. You know, vegetables, fruit, lamb, beef, pork, fish. Taste of the countryside.'
'What, when we can buy frozen? You must be joking.'
'I only thought . . .'
'I'll do the thinking. Why go to the trouble of buying fresh

67

and having to cut bits off, wash it, prepare it, and stuff like that? They can have it unfrozen and like it. Just as good, you know.'

'Do you really think so?'

'No, but I'm not eating it am I? Half of them don't know what good food is anyway. They like soggy pasta, mushy veg and re-heated meat. It's what they get at home. Sprinkle a bit of parsley on it and give the tomatoes spiky edges and they think they're living.'

'If you say so. What about the sweet trolley?'

'Oh, the usual. They'd be disappointed if there wasn't Black Forest gateau, and you can keep it for ages. Tinned fresh fruit salad. Strawberry surprise.'

'What's the surprise?'

'There's no strawberries in it. A bit of sweaty cheese and a few crackers, some lukewarm coffee and a handful of after-dinner mints – it's the little touches, the attention to detail, that brings them back to get taken in again. Give them after-dinner mints and they'll forget everything else, mark my words.'

'Well, I think that covers everything. Oh, I nearly forgot – the canned music, we'd better get that organised.'

'Good thinking. It gives them something to hum along to while they're waiting. As I say, it's the little touches that make the difference. Bon appetit as we say in the trade.'

It's hard to see light side

The problem with seeing the funny side of life as often as possible is that people may think you're a half wit.

It's like the remark made about politicians and bureaucrats in the EEC: 'Anyone who isn't confused simply does not know what's going on.'

In the same way if you find life and farming funny then you simply don't realise how serious it all is: this isn't a rehearsal, you know, it's a one innings game.

All the more reason then for enjoying it as much as possible, which isn't easy. It is usually easier to be serious and miserable particularly at this time of year when farm dispersal sales are a daily occurrence in the north and the Borders.

They may be slightly less downhearted affairs than those of last summer with prices slightly better, but not by much. A dispersal is never cheerful unless the farmer is retiring full of health and vigour to do something more worthwhile.

As most farmers refuse to believe there is anything more worthwhile than farming it follows that most of them refuse to retire unless forced into it by ill health, lack of money or 'family pressure' which can take many forms from a depressed wife to a son with a shotgun.

When death or lack of money is the reason it doesn't give a dispersal a cheerful start. Much of the conversation at the sale revolves round the reason for it being held with the farmer's character and personality coming out of the exchanges better if he had the sense to die rather than go bust.

Whatever the reasons, dispersals are thick on the ground again this summer. They are one of many signs that our rural way of life is changing.

I don't say that lightly because change in farming is a continuous process as it is in most industries and homes.

There has always been great debate about whether farming should think of itself as another industry or as a way of life.

I suspect we all like to project ourselves as businessmen while secretly thinking we have a rather different, quite enjoyable way of life. If we didn't think that we would be as well not to bother because no one asks us to soldier on being miserable and moaning about our lot.

But dispersal sales are only the most public indication of changes as the screw tightens.

Recently many farm houses have been on the market as 'Des. res. 6 bdrm., 2 pblc. etc.' Sometimes the ten-acre house field or three-acre croft is thrown in as an extra inducement while the rest of the farm is sold to neighbours.

Splitting up farm land and buildings is not a good sign for the long term. It means existing farms are getting bigger and the empires are expanding.

Farm cottages are being sold as the work force is paid off. Rural unemployment increases and the population of what is already one of the most thinly populated areas in Britain dwindles further.

The services like public transport get thinner on the ground. Village schools close down. It is difficult to maintain a thriving community.

Ancillary industries which rely on farming also feel the draught. Machinery firms have been paying off sales staff and mechanics. Feed and fertiliser firms are doing the same; we have lost two good feed reps in the space of a month, one made redundant for the second time in a year.

The personal touch is disappearing as the computer and the accountant take over. The come and go approach to farm trading has been and gone.

Miss the pay-by date on the invoice now and there is no question of the rep picking it up some time. There's the stern reminder from head office computer followed by the 'Without prejudice' missive from their personal firm of debt collectors.

70

It's a bit much for a puncture repair, but there you are –
business is deadly serious and what was once good for a
laugh is now good for a writ:
'You are charged with sending a facetious rejoinder to the
debt collecting company regarding an appropriate use for
their demand. Do you plead guilty or not guilty:'
   I'd love to plead guilty. I only hope they took the advice.
No wonder it's hard to see the lighter side.

Machine age

Man is born to trouble as the sparks fly upward – this is doubly true if machinery is involved.

Murphy's law sums this up neatly: 'If anything can go wrong, it will.' O'Toole's Corollary adds: 'Murphy is an optimist.'

The truth of these laws is borne in on us very quickly, particularly on a farm. For example, I have the written proof of a letter sent to my late grandfather when I was six: 'We were going to lift potatoes today. The digger broke down. Dad fixed it. When the wheel fell off the tractor he was not very pleased.'

I bet he wasn't. It would be a wise collie that kept out of the way when he was putting the wheel back on.

I don't remember that incident. But I do remember quite clearly the facts of life about machinery being explained to me by a relative in East Lothian.

It was harvest time and two of us were young and on holiday. The sun, which older readers may remember, was beating down. Barley straw was positively crackling in the heat and the air was full of the sounds of combines clattering up and down fields. Except in the farmyard we were in.

The combine stood silent. Occasionally another piece of metal, a few links of chain or a bolt or two flew into the air from the vicinity of the engine and drum and landed on the ground.

The youngest member of the farm staff was tiptoeing round collecting these bits and putting them in a neat heap. It was reaching quite an impressive size.

Various snorting, snarling, bellowing and banging noises could be heard from the combine's innards and there were occasional clouds of dust and chaff. The heat was intense and the nearest field of heavy-ripe barley was shimmering in the haze.

We watched fascinated. After a few minutes there was a final crescendo of snorting, snarling and bellowing, and our relative began to appear. He was a big, burly chap who had to come out like a stage escapologist.

Like them, his backside came first, then somehow his boots and trousers and finally he levered himself out by his arms. He was never an oil painting, but this was something else.

His hair stood up like Stan Laurel's. His face, arms, neck and shirt were a mass of dust and grease. One eye was jammed shut with muck and the other was savagely bloodshot. He looked at the sky, at the heap of bits and pieces, at the dead-ripe barley, then began to talk to himself in a low voice.

Another voice, young and piping, broke the silence:
'Is there something wrong with it?'

On reflection, I've asked more sensible questions at more suitable times. My brother, who has faster reactions, was starting to move before I'd finished speaking, and the farm lad already had a five-yard start on him.

The fact that I'm still here to tell the tale is probably attributable to all passion being spent – or nearly all. The one bloodshot eye pinned me to the spot as two big hands began to fondle, lovingly, the hammer they were holding.

It took him a little time to set his mind in order. Then he spoke:
'How old are you now?'
'T . . . t . . . ten.'

He considered this. Ten seemed to be old enough.
'In that case, this machine is . . .'

Some of the words were quite new to me then, but as he warmed to his theme I got the general idea. When he saw he had convinced me that, in his honest opinion, the combine was unfit for scrap metal he stopped speaking.

I walked quietly away as he began to pick parts of the combine at random to hit with the hammer. It wasn't many years later before I began to realise how he felt and particularly one thing – telling me what was wrong was the easy part. The really hard part was not bouncing the hammer off my head.

Holidays down on the farm

On-farm holidays now provide many farmers with a welcome supplementary income. Caravan and camping sites show an enviable cash-crop return per acre, while renting cottages or farmhouse rooms or providing bed and breakfast show a smaller but still worthwhile return.

And there should be no complaint about a worthwhile return for the farmer if the holiday-maker is convinced that the facilities and services provided represent money well spent.

Unfortunately some people need more convincing than others. For the increasing number of farmers thinking of going into the holiday business, and for the increasing number of holidaymakers weaned on Continental sun-spot package tours who fancy a change, this is a cautionary tale.

The cottage in question, one of those now listed by the Scottish Tourist Board as self catering accommodation, stands on a disused railway line in the Borders.

At the time of our venture, the late 1960s, it lacked 'amenities' – that is, no electricity and no flush toilet. The procession of British Rail employees who had lived in it through the preceding 60 or 70 years had also to carry their own water from a well 400 yards away, but that problem had been solved by running a pipe from the main farm supply and fitting sink units.

We provided the furniture, the cutlery, the plates, logs for the fire if the summer nights turned chilly, a gas stove, oil lamps, a potential escort service for eligible females and a disposal team to collect garbage and empty the 'outback' Elsan closets.

Perhaps the fact that the Elsan closet emptiers doubled up as the escorts never gave that service a fair chance. Be that as it may, the cottage was barely a mile from the village, two miles from the river, ten miles from the sea and no further to the Cheviot hills. To a country eye it seemed to offer most things expected of a country holiday.

We knew, of course, that with a direct choice a holidaymaker would choose the Hilton. On the other hand they weren't being offered the Hilton for a week for a family for £5. Even in the late 1960s £5 seemed a modest sum to charge.

The first family stayed a week and grumbled steadily – mainly, I think, because they were our first clients and we made the mistake of hovering around each day like a head waiter looking for a tip, asking if everything was all right. Naturally, they became suspicious that something was wrong and in their efforts to find it, they claimed energetically that everything was.

We provided a potty for the little girl who couldn't go outside to the toilet at night, and a new seat for the closet for father who could. We provided a new batch of logs because it was cold, then spent two hours with a hammer and chisel opening a window because the room got too hot.

We filled and lighted their oil lamps, pulled their car to start it, moved several placid bullocks out of an adjoining field because the kids were terrified, and finally provided a rope to make the same children a swing in the fervent hope that the father would hang himself while making it. The only damage he received was rope burns when sliding down triumphant from the branch – and for that we provided cold cream.

Net loss on the week, discounting any return on capital we had expected on the modest sum paid for the cottage, was about £3. If that continued through the summer we would, we decided, be better to pull the cottage down and build a lean-to hay shed.

We tried to learn from our mistakes with the next family. No more playing the head waiter, no more appearing like a genie from a bottle at the first hint of a jammed window or flat battery, no more feeling guilty about the weather or the prices in the local shops.

76

That family spent most of their week in Berwick, comparing it unfavourably with Callella, and left a day early taking the last of the logs and the potty with them. At least we made some profit that week.

The third family lasted only two days. Ostensibly, they left because a bedroom wall was running with damp. Actually the damp spot was about dinner-plate size.

The man simply refused to admit he had made a tactical mistake by bringing his widowed mother-in-law along. Again we made a profit, as they didn't ask for a refund, but being reasonably conscientious we were unhappy about the way our holiday home was progressing.

In fact, things did improve from then on, and one or two groups actually seemed to enjoy themselves, notably an elderly couple who went fishing each day and a sextet of youngsters who went on route marches from dawn to dusk through the neighbouring countryside. Strangely enough, they were also the only ones who didn't complain about the lack of laid-on entertainment and professed thoroughly to enjoy the local Friday night village hall dance.

But at the end of that summer we decided enough was enough. As things had gone, we stood more chance of making a worthwhile return by going to the local dance each week ourselves and buying a bunch of raffle tickets.

The cottage has now been fully modernised at astronomical cost and let at similar rates quite successfully.

It apparently does not pay to offer self-catering accommodation at a low rent which involves any self sufficiency. It is better to provide a cottage with all the conveniences people are used to at a much higher rent, which they will pay quite happily.

The possibilities are there for farmers to make some extra income; the possibilities are also there for many of our 90 per cent urban population to enjoy a country holiday. Both categories, however, should avoid looking for miracles.

Barley field fire proves seeing is not believing

There are times when it is not possible to believe your eyes. When I saw the row of straw behind the combine burst into flames, it was one of those times.

We were cutting a 25-acre field of Tipper winter barley which was yielding fairly well. We started it on the last day of the dry spell in these parts when it was coming off the combine at an unbelievable 12% moisture content; we've never had anything less than 15% before.

Then we were held up by two days of heavy rain and went back to finish the last six or seven acres at the beginning of the week. One lorry load was filled and emptied without incident and the first combine tankful of the next load safely augered in.

Angus cut down one side of the break and started cutting back up through the other. I was sitting in the lorry waiting for him to reach the point where we would start emptying again. That was when I could not believe my eyes.

I've heard of people sitting transfixed, but I never appreciated what it meant until I sat looking at the flames shooting up and already starting to move down the row, fanned by a strong, western breeze.

Then I bawled at Angus through the CB and he was beating out flames within seconds. However, that did not work so he tried cutting swathes cross-over.

I set off in the lorry for the steading where the sprayer was on a tractor and about three-quarters full of water. That seemed like foresight, but was actually because we'd had a burst water main in the area two days before and had to water the pigs by tanker.

79

Throwing tractor and sprayer along the rutted track towards the billowing black smoke I still couldn't believe it was happening.

Once into the field with Angus sitting on the sprayer directing the jet we tried to head off the fire from the standing crop of spring barley through the hedge.

Once, veering too quickly to get close enough to the hedge, I jammed the wheels then the gear lever while the flames licked closer.

Somehow we got going again and cut off the fire at one stretch of hedge only for it to spurt ahead further along.

Fighting a fire your heart is always in your mouth. I've had two close calls in the past when burning straw has got out of control and had vowed I would never take chances again.

I hadn't, this fire was a complete and still unexplained accident, but the feeling of helplessness is the same.

It isn't exactly fear, although with the flames licking hungrily and the smoke choking me, there is a bit of fear in it.

Mostly it is bitter anger that such a raging flame can develop from what can only have been one spark.

Two fire engines arrived and even then we had another 20 minutes of heart-stopping, strength-sapping fight against it. More than once I thought flames had gone through the hedge.

Eventually, we beat it. The firemen went round methodically hosing out the last embers and the smoke gradually cleared. We looked at each other and what had been about five acres of standing barley.

Cutting a swath cross-over upwind of the original outburst had saved about two acres. In total, we lost about three acres of crop and five or six acres of straw so it didn't even qualify as a big fire compared with one a few miles away last week when about 40 acres went up.

That didn't make us feel much better. It was more than big enough for us and the fact that we weren't in any way to blame didn't make us feel any better.

Even when it was all over I found myself like the farmer shown an elephant for the first time and walking away

shaking his head and saying:
'Impossible. No such animal.'

I felt like walking away slowly to take off my filthy shirt and trousers, have a bath and say:
'Impossible. No such fire.'

But looking at the forlorn black stems of straw sticking up and the seven or eight tonnes of barley heads on the ground I couldn't convince myself.

I should have known it was going to be that sort of day. The JCB got a flat tyre when we were giving big bales to the bulls and there was a threatening letter from a tradesman.

On his statement was one of those friendly little stickers to jog your memory about overdue accounts, although this one actually wasn't overdue at the time I got the statement.

But this sticker said menacingly:
'We subscribe to D & B Ltd – Commercial Collection Division.'

Things have come to a pretty pass when the local tradesmen put the frighteners on for £2.76.

A vetching question?

One of the many crops we have never grown, and have no intention of growing, is Old English Vetch.

This would not have worried me at all if an invoice for 1.5 tonnes of Old English Vetch seed had not appeared in the post.

At first glance I thought the price was quite reasonable, and wondered if it was a code-name for a new variety of wheat. Then I wondered what anyone would do with 1.5 tonnes of the seed. Then I wondered why they had sent the invoice to us.

In the normal run of things at this time of year there are quite enough invoices appearing for goods which we have bought without getting someone else's.

I knew what the reason would be of course, and it was – the computer. Now I have to wait until the computer sends us a credit to cancel the invoice for the Old English Vetch seed which we never had in the first place.

It was the same computer which charged us haulage for the oilseed rape, which had already been paid by us to the haulier. Come to think of it, it was the same computer which charged us twice for the same load of feed barley.

It was that transaction which really showed up the computer for what it is – a sophisticated abacus which works absolutely according to programme and has no glimmering of commonsense.

The load of barley was 7.790, a trailer load we collected ourselves. Almost any human sending out invoices would have realised that it was most unlikely anyone could collect two loads of precisely 7.790 tonnes, but a realisation like that is beyond a computer and it accordingly sent two identical invoices.

Again we had to wait until the computer sent us a credit for 7.790 tonnes to eradicate its own mistake. I lived in hope that it would lose the place completely and send two credits for 7.790 tonnes, but the mistakes only seem to occur one way.

We've been having the same problem with machinery bills. A lengthy list of those 'bits and pieces' for combines, tractors and swathers which mount up into four figures over harvest arrived, on time, as usual.

When we checked it, as usual, several items should not have been listed at all, such as parts covered by warranty. The salesman's reason was illuminating: 'It would have to be somebody like you that checked right through it – it must be the computer.'

They sent it back to the computer with fresh instructions. It came in this morning, amended certainly, but with charges added for the delay.

I re-addressed the envelope to the firm with a scribbled instruction of my own for the computer and am waiting with interest to see what it makes of it. If it can't cope I may ask to talk to it as **IBM** have now 'persuaded' a computer to recognise spoken sentences from a 5,000 word vocabulary.

It seems the computer prefers a short pause between each word for maximum impact, which would suit my present mood perfectly and, even better, words not stored in the computer's vocabulary can be understood if spelled out slowly.

Tight, set phrases giving simple instructions are said to be best. I can hardly wait to meet one.

Another crop we haven't grown so far is winter oats. This may soon put us in a minority as several hundred acres of the crop have been drilled within a few square miles.

Anticipated yields of more than 50 cwt. an acre with lower spray and fertiliser costs than winter wheat or winter barley and an anticipated higher price seem to be the main reasons.

With the ball on the slates as far as most cereal crops are concerned, any kind of premium must be worth looking for but I would think that several hundred extra acres of winter oats next harvest must affect any possible bonus.

As with so many things in farming we must wait and see. One thing we have not had to wait for this autumn has been the dramatic greening-up of stubble fields; I'm not sure what the main causes are, but virtually every grain of spring or winter barley which went over the back of the combine or was cut off at ground level, must have germinated.

Any not ploughed in provides useful grazing, but the thick green growth on what should be bare stubble is a galling sight. I only hope it's not Old English Vetch.

A class of their own

'As part of their project our class visited a typical farm on a typical harvest day last week. These are the stories they wrote about it which I have chosen to put on the wall:
'Farmers are very kind to their sheep. They like them to get a lot of exercise. That is why the farmer was coming up the road behind his sheep tooting his horn. He said this was to let them know he was still there in case they got worried. He shouted to Miss Penfold to open the gate and she did it quite quickly once she'd worked out only one of the four bits of string was really keeping it shut.
'But by then the sheep had gone through a hole. The farmer said this was a short cut, ha ha and banged his head on the windscreen. Then we went for a walk round the farm.'
'Pigs are quite clean. But they smell. I was sick and had to come out. When I came out my friend Helen came out as well. When she came out Wilma came out. Then Lorraine. And Sharon. And Ann. We were all standing feeling sick and the boys were laughing at us. Then Robert Wilson, serve him right, stood in something and he stopped laughing and came hopping out. Miss Penfold was trying to say something to the farmer, but the pigs were squealing so loudly they came out as well. I'm going to be a vegetarian.'
'The tractor was ace, but we weren't allowed on it. Robert Wilson nearly got his foot under the wheel when Miss Penfold was not looking, but the man in the tractor saw him. He was moving it very slowly and stopped. He said something to Robert Wilson. I'n not sure what it was, but I heard my dad say it once when he got his finger stuck in my bike chain. Robert Wilson is a pretty fast runner. I want to be a lorry driver.'
'A lorry was in for a load of grain. The farmer said watch this

it will be interesting. It took ages to turn round and the farmer said to Miss Penfold some folk could not reverse a wheelbarrow ha ha. And the lorry driver shouted something out of the window at him and the farmer had a little chat while Miss Penfold was telling us to come and look at the lovely cow. It licked Lorraine's face and she started crying again.

'Then the farmer came up and Miss Penfold said what lovely cows and he said bullocks and she went all huffy and said we'd better look at something else then. The forklift loading the lorry was bril. When he missed the side and put a scoopful on the ground we all got handfulls and threw it at each other. The farmer said he was testing to see if there was much in the big bin by banging his head against it.'

'We went to a farm. We went to a field. It had a combine thing in it. It was not going. It was stuck. The end.'

'My project was on how we make bread. The farmer said with great difficulty this year ha ha. However, we could see his combine cutting wheat he said. This would be the first stage in making bread if the millers played the white man about Hapsburgs and didn't try to hide their price under a bushell ha ha.

'He seemed to think this was pretty funny and kept laughing and explaining it to Miss Penfold till we got to the field where the combine was supposed to be cutting. But it was just sitting there sunk in the mud. A man walked past us and said to the farmer that he'd told him it was too something wet. 'Miss Penfold said that 'something' was a technical term connected with bread-making wheat and the farmer muttered that was something true. Lorraine was making notes but Miss Penfold said not to bother. It didn't look as if the wheat in that field would make very good bread. I don't like bread much anyway, specially the crusts."

'When it started raining again they put a wire rope on the combine and pulled it with a tractor. When the tractor sank they put another rope on it and pulled with the forklift. A wire rope makes a funny noise when it snaps like that. Farmers can walk very quickly in dirty wellingtons. Miss Penfold could hardly keep up and Lorraine was crying again.

'The same sheep were on the road again and the farmer said wouldn't you think they'd had enough exercise for one day then started running after them like crazy. You have to be fit to be a farmer.'

'Coming home in the minibus was best except that Robert Wilson still had some of that stuff on his feet and the driver made him get out again and clean his shoes on the grass. Miss Penfold said it had been most interesting and the farmer said yes hadn't it we must come again sometime and learn more about the joy and pleasure of farming.

'When we left he was banging his head against the gatepost and Miss Penfold said this was a countryman's way of finding out whether it was going to rain. But it was raining anyway. I want to be an air hostess.'

Taste of the real world

I suppose I spend as much time doing the shopping as the average farmer – probably once a year in a good year.

By 'shopping' I mean buying groceries, not pottering about looking at leggings, caps and aerosols in various farming supply shops or wandering about the bargain centre at the Highland show.

I should do it more often, if I only had the time, because it is fascinating to see what foods people actually buy as opposed to what farmers think they should buy.

What we think they should buy is naturally all grown in Britain and they should buy plenty of it, particularly delicious red meat.

They should also stuff themselves with bread and biscuits to maintain a quality wheat premium worth the name and, I suppose, drink huge qualtities of beer and whisky if there is to be a malting barley market at all.

Judging by the carry-outs, beer and whisky sales seem to be holding up and some farmers certainly do their best to prop up the market for malt.

But many other shopping baskets and trollies do not hold a lot for our comfort.

I base these findings only on estimates and approximations. Trying to inspect the shopping basket of some unsuspecting lady too closely can produce an icy stare or even a poke on the nose.

But surreptitious study suggests that shoppers fall into two categories. Correction, three categories. There is the type of shopper farmers like to see, the type they don't like to see and then there are male shoppers.

I don't write that lightly, but it's patently obvious to anyone that most male shoppers haven't a clue, including farmers.

Someone who moans like fury about his lamb prices being down a penny a kilo, an extra £1 on tax off that week's wages for some reason or threepence on the price of petrol will take a shopping trolley round a supermarket as if he was Paul Getty or an agricultural chemicals salesman.

We may as well have two packets of that; oh, stick in another one, there doesn't look much there; we haven't had that for a while; go on, try it; I'm sure this used to be in bigger tins, better take four; five of us will eat more meat than that. And so on. They look pained when the cashier adds it up, even when she hasn't made a mistake.

This finding, based on a random sample, has been confirmed by a source close to home and can be verified further by any wife.

That leaves the good shopper and the shopper who is not so good from our point of view. What I think of as the good shopper buys beef, lamb and pork, milk, potatoes, fresh vegetables, eggs and fish.

Admittedly fish farms don't produce a tremendous share of the market and salmon poachers don't need any help from me, but I've always thought that ordinary fishermen, at sea in most weathers, more than earn their money.

What you are more likely to see in the average shopping basket will be a range of tins and packets, a frozen chicken or chicken portions, packets of frozen vegetables, soft drinks, sweets and cakes.

I suppose that somewhere along the line farming is picking up a small share of the total retail value of a basketful like that, but it won't be much. Whoever sells sugar and preservatives will be making more.

And don't take my small-sample word for it. Look at any report on our national diet during the past few years or any television programme on food in the past few months.

They will say that half our diet consists of, basically, rubbish salted, sweetened or flavoured to make it attractive and that the other half is not good for us, including full fat milk, meat with fat on it or in it, white bread and so on.

We are told by the health-food enthusiasts and the organic

popularisers that the tide is turning. There is a new interest in diet and health and fewer people are now intent on digging their grave with their teeth.

I don't see it. Not yet anyway. There may be a small change, but the eating habits of years don't change as dramatically as the enthusiasts would have us believe.

And even if they do change, from the purely selfish farming view, where does that leave us?

Well behind, apparently, in our attempts to persuade the housewife, or consumer if you prefer, to buy more of what we produce. We may be reasonably good at producing, but we are very poor at marketing, either doing it ourselves or paying professionals to do it for us.

Doing the shopping more often is a very small start.

My cup runneth over

If all the people who have ever produced home-made wine were laid end to end I wouldn't be at all surprised.

Statistically, if all the millions of gallon jars with two lugs and rubber stoppers which are hiding in lofts, garages, coalsheds, granaries and cupboards all over Britain were laid end to end they would probably reach the moon.

My contribution would be about a dozen and I won't ask for any offers; what usually happens when I mention the subject is that I get offered more which I don't want.

It is true that I did at one time. I was impressed by the idea of living among so much natural material which was just right for wine making.

I was even more impressed by the image of home-made wine conjured up by H. E. Bates in his Uncle Silas stories – the clear, limpid beauty of elderflower, the red ruby glow of the elderberry.

I'm not much of a drinker, but my mouth started to water at the thought – or should it be that my palate started to tremble. Whichever it was, it seemed that very little could be simpler than to collect masses of elderflower, add the water and a few pounds of sugar, plus some liquid yeast and wait for the clear and limpid beauty of the liquid to appear.

I should have been warned by the amount of wine making equipment which was available in the area among friends and relatives. They all seemed quite keen that I should have it, with no hurry to hand it back.

Some pressed gallon jars on me without reservation. They didn't, they said, intend to make any more themselves for some time. They felt they had enough in stock to be going on with.

I remember being enthralled with the project. We

collected several tons of elderflowers, carefully stripped them off the green stems, boiled the water and sugar as prescribed and then poured the liquid over the flowers and added lemon juice.

It was the first time that I'd ever felt kindly towards the elder tree, otherwise known as bourtree and liable to appear in old steadings or neglected hedges.

In fact, I stayed keen for some time, watching the elderflower 'wine' develop, siphoning clear liquid off the rubbish – or racking off the lees as we afficianados say – and generally behaving like any other do it yourself half-wit.

And all the time the words of the book on wine-making ran through my head:
'Wine-making in the home is a simple and inexpensive hobby. It is easy to make a drinkable wine with a limited knowledge of the processes involved.'

How true, I thought, how true. Every time I siphoned off the liquid and watched it become more limpid, I swallowed a few mouthfuls. In retrospect, they were the only ones worth drinking but luckily, as with so many of life's disappointments, I didn't know that at the time.

Eventually with the elderflower safely bottled and being left for at least 12 months to mature I began to turn my attention to other gifts of nature.

Dandelions, for instance. If there was plenty of elderflower about there was a positive abundance of dandelions. We collected a lot, put it in a bucket and poured the obligatory gallon of boiling water over it.

I knew the smell which gradually began to envelop first the back porch then the kitchen and finally most of the house reminded me of something. Eventually it came to me – pig mash. Returning to the book I read:
'The beginner should not be frightened off by all the jargon that goes with wine-making and should be comforted by the knowledge that even the most experienced person has an off day.'

That was it. I'd had an off day. I poured the pig mash out in a corner of the hen run and the hens huddled as far away from it as they could.

I got further with the pea pod wine, persuaded once again by the abundance of free material. More gallon jars, rubber stoppers, lengths of siphoning tubing, Camden tablets, dried yeast, dozens of empty bottles and all the other paraphenalia which goes with the hobby had come my way in the past few weeks.

I wanted to make several gallons of pea pod, but was asked politely not to. It was suggested that several gallons of fermenting pea pods might make the house a little crowded and something, or someone, else might have to go.

Pea pods don't taste much eaten raw. They taste even less when masquerading as wine. I think I'd racked it twice, tasting as I went, before I gave up and threw it out.

My enthusiasm was waning a little when harvest and autumn drilling came along and I had time to forget. When the season of mists and mellow fruitfulness came along I was ready to go again.

We made bramble wine, apple cider, potato wine, wheat wine and finally the one I'd been waiting for – elderberry.

We spent hours at night siphoning, bottling, gargling with these wines, yodelling with them, corking bottles, delighting in nature's bounty.

With several shelves full we began to try them out during the next year or so. They were uniformly, with barely an exception, awful.

Nature may provide, but my wine making was lousy. We've managed to dispose of most of the equipment, but I keep a few gallon jars and some odds and ends in case I ever get the urge again.

And just in case I do I also keep a few bottles of what we made when we were enthusiasts. We never drink it, but it removes gloss paint very efficiently.

May the force be with you

My father's expression for it used to be 'try a bit of Ferguson.' This referred to the method popular among amateur mechanics, when most other things have failed, of hitting a piece of machinery with a hammer.

It has to be said, however, that his expression for the farming equivalent of hitting the television or punching the car door came from a professional mechanic many years ago.

It happened quite simply as many of these one-farm or one-family expressions do, although it was a bit unfair on the tractor pioneer Harry Ferguson.

At the time we had one of the little grey Fergusons. Most farms in Britain had one at some time in the 1940s and 1950s and pound for pound they were one of the best tractors ever produced.

Like the Morris 1000 or the Mini, anyone who ever had one still has a soft spot for the Ferguson. They had that essential factor that only the very best tractors have of pulling more than their weight and of doing more than you can reasonably expect of them.

They were also nippy, uncluttered and easy to drive. There was a one, two, three, four gearstick plus reverse which could be mastered by the least able among us.

Before the death toll on farms related to tractors and machinery accidents became so prominent, many of us learned to drive a Ferguson at a very early age. They were also reliable.

When they did break down, repairs were fairly straightforward. Except on the occasion which produced the saying when the mechanic had tried several approaches before an audience.

Eventually he sent his audience of two in different

directions on trumped-up errands. I was asked to go for an oil can, my father was asked if he would mind phoning to see if such and such a part was in the stores.

The sound of hammer blows seemed to start soon after we crossed the yard. Coming back with the oil can as quickly as possible and without troubling to make the phone call we found the mechanic cheerfully, if slightly guiltily, holding a freed part in one hand and a stout hammer in the other. 'Surprising what a bit of Ferguson can do,' he said before getting on with the repair. The saying stuck whenever we resorted to the same method ourselves, but the results have not always been so successful.

And not just unsuccessful for us. A fine example of what not to do was the old grain drill where a main cog which was supposed to slide into various positions on a shaft had jammed solid over winter.

Oil, releasing fluid and gentle persuasion having failed, my father and I looked at each other and started to reach for the hammer at the same time. Then we thought better of it and phoned for a mechanic.

The mechanic came, saw, and reached for a hammer. Then he thought better of it and placed a block of wood between the cog and the hammer. Then he hit it as hard as he could. And the cast metal cog split in half in exactly the same way as it would have done if I had hit it.

Mechanics can get quite huffy when they hear you muttering 'I could have done that' under your breath. But it was true, I could have done it. And have.

The problem is the fine dividing line between a judicious whack, or possibly two or three, to get something moving, remove a jammed bolt, seized spring or any of the thousand and one other things which can go wrong with machinery and insane hammering.

It may be that others occasionally reach the stage I reach of taking one last savage swing in the full knowledge that the result is as likely to be bad as it is to be good.

If there are any, I know how they feel – that after so much effort, sweat and bad temper, something will happen and to hell with it.

Knowing that I have this tendency, I can go to the other extreme of firm, but restrained taps in the belief that I am taking a professional approach.

Then someone steps in, asks if they can have a go, gives one almighty blow with a hammer, the jammed bolt flies out and I try not to bite my thumb off in frustration.

Throwing the hammer or spanner away in these circumstances does no good. It rebounds off a tyre and can leave you with a limp; there are many things to consider before trying a bit of Ferguson including 'a limp what?'

One task where patience and persuasion beat brute strength

There is one good thing to be said about loading pigs onto a lorry. It takes your mind off all other problems.

There are a lot of bad things to say about the job and most of them are every Monday morning as we push or carry them up the ramp.

To be fair, there are good mornings when the 10, 12 or 15 which are heavy enough to go, fairly race up the ramp and everyone heaves a sigh of relief.

But most of them don't like the ramp even when it is thickly spread with straw – which the lorry drivers don't like because it's more trouble to clean than sawdust. They particularly don't like the step at the top.

I can see their point. The step on the regular lorry doesn't look much to me, but for a 65 kilo pig with its short legs it is the equivalent of three stairs at a time.

The big pig carriers, who may transport several hundred, have solved this problem by fitting lifts on the back of their lorries. Pigs walk in to the lift at ground level then up they go to lorry deck level.

We have this idea for a pen built on a pallet which would hold six or eight pigs and be lifted to lorry level by the JCB. Either that or build a proper loading ramp.

Meantime, we're persevering with the rather makeshift set up at the Marldown steading as the last porkers go away from there.

Ironically, conditions in the old hen-battery seem to have suited them. They have grown quickly and have sold well recently, looking more like the long, lean pig we're told is needed.

The only bugbear has been drawing them out to weigh and then the loading. As with loading any livestock there is that frisson of tension as they move towards the ramp and that crucial moment when you find out whether it is going to be a good loading or a bad one.

That is when the ones in front, either cattle or pigs, pause to look at the ramp and the lorry and make their minds up whether they are going on or going back.

There is that sigh of relief as they decide to go on. Or the muttered curse as they decide to swing round or reverse and come back.

Half-a-dozen pigs can be handled with a door or sheet of tin behind them, but when 15 decide to come back it is difficult to hold up against a ton of pork on the trotter.

I know that because we've tried it and all that happens is your blood pressure rises and your eyes start to bulge.

Hitting them doesn't do any good either. It hurts your hand and the pigs don't feel it. Hitting them with anything else, though tempting, is unfair on the animal which simply doesn't like the metal surface underfoot after a life on straw.

It also leaves marks. So the only answer for all concerned is to calm down and try again to persuade them. That is the theory. I don't say we manage it every time, but we do try.

We've found the same approach works when moving sows from the service yard to the shed where all the pregnant sows are housed. I always have a tendency to try to rush them, moving in just too quickly with the final nudge or attempt to shut the gate.

What the sow does then, of course, is snort with alarm, jump back and set off in another direction. Looking at a sow you wouldn't imagine some of them could move so fast, swinging and wobbling in several directions at once like some over-optimistic marathon runner.

My tendency to rush is worse at this time of year when there are still several hundred jobs to do connected with harvest and autumn drilling. We've found the best time to move them, when the sows tend to be more amenable and I tend to be less frantic, is early in the cool and dampness of the morning.

End of the line for a branch road

For more years than I care to think about, the instructions for finding our farm have always included the phrase 'there's a small wood at the road-end.'

In time the wood will return, as the intention of the estate is to replant, but for a few years at least it will look strange without the triangular acre of trees.

Several other parts of the farm already look strange, as tree felling operations have been going on for about a month. The reason is the usual one of Dutch elm disease.

Almost all our field boundary trees are elm with the exception of a few ash and sycamore, even fewer oaks, and a solitary beech – and all the elm have the disease.

Several of the more twisted and elderly had become dangerous as dead branches snapped and fell. Others were going the same way, and the decision was taken to fell them all and replant with the estate supplying the trees and grow-tubes and us doing the planting.

If I had been less cack-handed with a chain saw I would have liked working with timber. Watching the professionals drop a tree and reduce it to a trimmed main trunk, other useful main branches, a pile of small branches for firewood, and a burning heap of trimmings is fascinating. When I had time to watch, that is.

We planned our cropping this autumn to accommodate them as much as possible and they obliged by getting into action as soon as fields were cut and cleared.

The result was a steady hum of activity on most parts of the farm, with everyone too busy with their own work to watch anyone else. Only occasionally did they coincide, like the day beside the gas sub-station which we have in the corner of one field just off the main road.

101

The vermicelli system of pipes in there was being sand blasted and repainted, which involved half a dozen men and a foreman. Three tree fellers – or just tree fellers if you're Irish – and a driver on the tractor with winch were starting work in the wood across the farm road.

Alan was clearing bales, and I was ploughing the cleared stubble. If that wasn't enough activity in one small corner, a tree grower also appeared on the scene.

He asked permission to bring his small lorry with raised platform into the field to pick sycamore seeds from the south side of the trees growing along the main road. Apparently, few seeds grow on the north side.

I would have agreed readily in any case, although it turned out that he was the grower who supplied our oak and sycamore saplings 18 months ago when we planted two acres of former railway banking.

He's coming out some weekend to see how they are getting on. With luck I'll get there before him and find out myself – as they have been one of the neglected areas in the past three months of slogging through the harvest and autumn drilling.

Watching him and his daughter at work provided one more variation to the day. Ploughing down the slope I had tree fellers on my right, and blasters and painters straight ahead.

Coming up, I had sycamore seed pickers ahead, and Alan on the right carting bales. The distractions may have had something to do with the elegant curve which developed in the ploughing and became more pronounced as the morning went on.

Picking lunchtime for the fellers and painters as the time to straighten the curve was not a good idea. Watching other people at work is fine, but others watching you while you're trying to correct mistakes is not much fun.

By the time the crowd gathered, however, I had started a series of short furrows to get rid of the curve. The technique consists of taking the longest straight end of the furrow and following it out into the area already ploughed, instead of following the bend which has developed.

At this time of year it is almost irrelevant anyway as the

field will be cultivated and drilled within a day or two, but I do like to plough in straight lines if possible. I hope the crowd appreciated that, although there was no burst of applause as I finally got back on to a straight the length of the field.

By then the front wheel had fallen off Alan's tractor, which brought proceedings to a temporary halt. When that was fixed everyone else was back to work and the seed collectors had gone. The biggest tree in the wood had also gone down unseen by me.

From then on, I concentrated on the ploughing, enjoying the sunshine, the whiff of woodsmoke, and the pleasure of an irrelevantly straight furrow.

Keep your light under a bushel

Now that so few of us take the trouble to go to the pictures we only tend to bore our own families or unfortunate visiting friends and relatives. I know, I do it myself.

Superman was an example when it appeared on our television at Christmas. As a fan of his from the *Marvel* comic days I was keen to see what they had done to Clark Kent and Lois Lane on film and wasn't disappointed.

But in one of the climactic scenes as the young Superman stood alone in the middle of a prairie, having just realised fully the extent of his powers, I couldn't restrain myself.

As the camera swept across several thousand acres of America while it steadily closed in on the mighty physique of Superman, I remarked:

'Look at the wild oats in that wheat.'

The family claim that I rose half out of my seat and shouted, but that must be an exaggeration. Possibly I raised my voice slightly to be heard above the theme music – and there were an awful lot of wild oats.

From the silence which greeted the remark and the long suffering looks from the children I realised, not for the first time, that the presence of wild oats or wickens in a grain crop does not interfere with their enjoyment of a programme.

The same is true of the breed of cattle used in Westerns. There are some which use the genuine Longhorn, but most use Hereford crosses on the cattle drives: apart from looking far too fat and fit to be on a 1000 mile drive through pesky Redskin country, the Hereford and Aberdeen Angus didn't become popular in America until the grazing improved.

Somehow not many people want to know that. Even in the days when cinema-going was more popular they didn't want to know as a large gentleman made clear to me one night when I was airing youthful knowledge.

I gathered during the course of his 30-second monologue that he didn't particularly care whether the cattle stampeding across Arizona were Longhorn, Shorthorn, Middlehorn or any kind of horn at all.

I thought of telling him there wasn't a breed called the Middlehorn, but the way he emphasised his remarks by bringing his fist down on the top of my head made me decide to leave him in ignorance of that fact and leave early. It wasn't much of a film anyway.

The main lesson this taught me was to choose my cinema seat more carefully, although it also moderated my desire to pass on what I thought of as valuable information to an unreceptive audience.

I decided that the great British public, or at least that part of it which went to the Playhouse in Berwick, could do without knowing the finer points of the Hereford or the Angus or that corn wasn't cut in June or that modern milking wasn't done with a bucket.

Or many more of the technical slip-ups which appeared in films then and still do. However, I made an exception for the film Tom Jones which contained a lot of country life on the squire's estate.

I did this on the principle which I'm told makes concert audiences clap after the first few notes of any piece that they aren't clapping the performer but themselves for recognising the music.

Likewise in Tom Jones when the squire threatened to make Tom eligible for the gelding's plate at the next race meeting. Few people in the audience that night were familiar with the term – gelding that is, not race meeting – so I laughed just long enough to show that I knew what it meant.

When the town-bred lads I was with asked what was funny, I explained quite graphically after first looking to see there were no big men with large fists sitting behind.

The lads thought it was quite funny too as I explained, but the two little old ladies I'd missed on my right weren't so impressed. At least they said they weren't, but I'm sure it gave them something to think about.

105

That was positively my last attempt to be informative in the cinema. Now I restrict myself to home ground and it is astonishing the number of times television programme makers focus lovingly in close up on wild oats of the botanic kind.

If you don't believe that, you're not concentrating closely enough. Either that or your family too have persuaded you that it doesn't really matter and that there is no real need for an agricultural adviser on every programme.

Getting it done – in comfort

On most farms there is a difference between things as they should be and things as they are.

In some cases this can be the same difference as there is between what the farmer fondly imagines things to be and what the visitor actually sees.

But most of us are aware of the differences even if we avoid thinking about them too much. We know that a 52 cwt wheat crop isn't a 70 cwt crop or that a pen of cattle gaining two lbs a day aren't gaining three lbs.

Or that a yard which should be concreted isn't. Or that several gates tied with string isn't a custom-built loading bay. The list may not be endless but it could go on for a long time.

Yet in this list one thing would probably still stick out more than any other – the farm office.

I know there are plush farm offices, usually on estates where the latest gadgetry to handicap efficiency can be installed. There are also efficient farm offices. Then there are the nooks and crannies in house or outbuildings where most of us work when forced to it.

They can be called functional for want of a better word, such as chaotic. Like the instant loading bay mentioned earlier they are usually aimed at being a place to get something done without lingering.

I recall an Agricultural Training Board course I went to some years ago when the urge to be efficient and proficient with the paper work was unusually strong. I think it was called office management and lasted two days.

The last hour or so, as light relief, we were invited to work in pairs and design our own office. It proved to be a revealing exercise.

My partner and I came up with an extremely spartan and functional room, based mainly on what we had at home as most of these things are.

It would help to get the work done all right, but was short on comfort. We had items like a cement floor to allow for the fact that a farm office is frequently used by people in a hurry with muddy boots or wellingtons on.

There may have been a chair, but as I prefer to stand at a fairly high desk when working, again there may not, except a functional one for visitors who were not expected to hang about.

Most of the designs were similar with great emphasis laid on working space and filing cabinets. Discussion centred round where to put the year-planner on the wall and how many different colours of pins were needed for the sheep recording chart.

By this time a senior sophisticated type was moaning softly and calling for strong drink. Seldom, he said, when asked to produce his own plans for an office, had he heard so much well meaning drivel.

What sort of an atmosphere were we intending to work in? Where was the comfort necessary for any kind of office work? Were we, in short, complete philistines?

Considering the company as I remember it the shorter answer to the last question was probably yes. We were nonplussed by any attempt to answer any of his other posers and waited with interest for his own ideas.

A pile carpet and muted lighting got him off to a good start. How different to the cement floor and fluorescent strip. The desk was naturally leather topped and the chair padded to a fault.

The outlook of his office would be the best available on the farm rather than facing directly onto the yard, the drying green or even windowless.

The working area was confined mainly to one corner and was the responsibility of a secretary who knew her place. For the rest of the office which was designed to be roughly the size of a small town hall, there were comfortable armchairs for welcome guests.

Unwelcome visitors wouldn't get as far as the office, he explained. They were dealt with in the yard or in the ante-room, preferably by electrocution.

For myself and the welcome visitors, the drinks cabinet played a prominent part. It was well stocked and regularly replenished.

He rather thought he might allow himself a calculator on the desk and a wall chart to keep track of the liquor supplies with possibly a telex to keep up to date on share prices and a computer to see how much he was losing on beef.

We all laughed obligingly. What sort of real farm office was that, I asked myself, being young and keen and functionally minded.

Now as I get older and consider the deep litter filing system at this frantic time of year, fighting as it is against the rising tide of grain samples, machinery manuals, fly sprays, nails, bolts, penicillin bottles, a syringe, two aerosols, two screwdrivers, a spanner, a broken bracket, a sample of turkey feed and a halter for a calf, I'm not so sure.

A pile carpet, comfortable chair and a well stocked liquor cabinet seem increasingly attractive. But they'll have to wait at least until next harvest.

A sporting chance

Blood sports don't figure much in The *Scottish Farmer*, unless you count Scottish Milk Marketing Board get-togethers with the distributive trade or Clydesdale breeders' special meetings.

There may not even be many hunting and fishing readers, but it is a fair bet that there will be quite a lot who know one end of a shotgun from the other – particularly at this time of year.

What they are able to do with it is another matter. Many farmers are good, or expert, shots. But for many more of us the walk round a rough pheasant shoot with friends, or even relatives, is still enjoyable whether or not we shoot much.

This is more so in some cases than others – like my own. For several years I used to carry a gun when we had our two or three walk-round shoots each winter.

In the course of several years I vividly remember shooting my first pheasant. This is no great feat of memory because it was also my last, and only.

This was not due to sudden revulsion against blood sports or sympathy for the birds. It's simply due to the fact that, although reasonably well co-ordinated in most things, I am damned if I can shoot.

It's something to do with aiming at where the bird is rather than where it will be when the shot arrives. At least I think that's it. Then, when I try to compensate by shooting at where I think it will be, the shot arrives yards ahead of the bird. Or something like that.

Whatever the reasons I eventually gave up being an embarrassment to myself and others with only that one bird to remember. Apart from anything else it must have been a very old and tired bird because it took as long to take off as a

110

Jumbo jet.

For some time I thought it wouldn't get airborne at all and, desperate as I was at that time to shoot something, anything, I couldn't bring myself to blast it on the ground. Rather unsporting I thought, with my trigger finger twitching.

Eventually it did get off the ground and rose slowly into the air across the line I was supposed to be covering. It's not really strange, but wherever I was stationed on a shoot, that was where most pheasants seemed to fly.

It's on the same principle as a sportsman having a bad day, I suppose. The ball follows him around as the catches continue to go down or the ball slides and slices off his boot.

Occasionally, shoot organisers had tried to make use of the way I attracted pheasants to my position by stationing a good shot right beside me. The theory was that the pheasants, by whatever telepathy they used, would search me out as their usual escape route. At which point the good shot would blast them out of the sky.

It never seemed to work like that. The pheasants would steer clear of us both. Until, that is, the good shot was moved and then back they would come again. So, as usual, I was on my own and the venerable pheasant obviously thought he was coasting it as he passed with his arthritic joints creaking.

The more unkind of those present on the historic occasion said that only one pellet was actually found in the deceased. It had simply been the shock of any pellet at all hitting him that had finished the old bird off. Pure and simple heart attack.

I didn't mind. They could say what they liked, and usually did. I'd got a pheasant at last even though there was not a lot of eating on it and I don't much care for it anyway.

I did think of having it stuffed, but thought that was carrying professional pride too far. I just thought about it often, particularly as the months and shooting seasons went past and I never shot another.

There were some close things though. More than once I was certain I'd seen a leg drop after I shot. But I was assured that the bird was simply scratching itself.

Finally, I did get another one, but it was a 'runner' which, once down, took off on two legs. We never found it and after that I quit. Not being able to hit them at all was bad enough, but hitting them and leaving them wounded was worse.

Not only that, I felt if I couldn't do it reasonably well I'd rather not do it at all. Now I enjoy the walk round, doing a certain amount of beating and quite a lot of talking, while the real sportsmen shoot the birds.

I don't go as far as the fox hunters and say that the pheasants enjoy it. But wild, fit pheasants on rough shooting have a reasonable chance I always think. True, they have less chance than before now that I have been replaced by someone who can actually shoot, but they still have a chance.

And farmers being what they are, two guns are just as liable to be discussing how this field of winter wheat is looking when the pheasants come steaming past as they are to be on full alert. There are worse ways to spend a winter Saturday.

Seasonal tails

It occurred to the old man as he struggled into his heavy working clothes that this was a ridiculously early start for anyone.

As he poured a last cup of tea before buttoning up his coat and putting on his wellingtons he decided that this would definitely be his last year in the job. Definitely.

Expertly he flicked the last dregs of tea into the sink and the mug flew off the handle to smash on the floor. He sighed and threw the handle on the floor as well. It looked like being another one of those days.

It was. Outside it was raining again and the glaur oozed and sucked around his wellingtons. More than that their soles were so worn and thin that he felt every ridge and stone as he picked his way across by the wavering light of the pencil torch he carried.

'I told the lazy beggars to get this yard cleaned up for Christmas,' he muttered ploughing on. Halfway across the battery finally failed and he walked face first into a fork somebody had left sticking in a bale at the shed door.

'I'll melt them,' he said savagely rubbing his glowing nose. 'I'll make them wish they worked for a living instead of skiving about here like a bunch of fairies.'

But once inside the shed out of the steady dripping rain he felt better. There was a hint of summer in the smell of good hay, a hint of harvest in the freshness of the barley straw the stock were lying on, a warm animal smell nearby.

'Damn,' he muttered, wiping off his wellington on a piece of straw.

'First covered with mud then covered with that. Still they say it's lucky. Ho, Ho.'

He laughed without much mirth and started walking up

the shed slapping backsides all the way to get them on their feet.

'Come on you idle beggars. Let's get the show on the road. It's a big delivery morning.'

One by one he unfastened them and led them out of their stalls and flicked the leather harnesses into place and collars over their heads.

He hardly blood-blistered his fingers at all in the chains but giving an extra yank on a head collar he snapped it. He murmured gently to himself about being too old for all this and repaired it with a bit of plastic string.

It was still raining as he led the team outside after giving them a quick once over. They were satisfactory but not much more. Staff these days didn't seem to take the same pride and care in keeping the harness in good condition or spending their own time on grooming the animals.

'Damn and blast,' he shouted as he walked into the fork again and his following team seemed to look at each other knowingly. The tantrums and bad temper were starting early. This could be a bad trip.

That seemed even more likely when he saw the way the cart was loaded with packages every which way and a definite lean to the left. On the first rope he checked the kinch knot fell apart in his hands and a big parcel bounced off his head onto the floor.

'I'll swing for that lot I will. Did you ever see anything like that in your life?'

Once the load was roped more to his satisfaction he backed the shivering team into it, climbed up onto the driving seat and urged them out into the rain and mud. At least that was the idea. The team stood straining and grunting but nothing happened.

'Overloaded again. Mind you, this lot couldn't pull a hen off the nest. Get up there. Get up.'

He roared out the order and cracked the nearest animal with a length of plastic piping he kept handy. This time the team leaped forward, the cart jerked and stotted, the traces snapped and the lead-two shot off into the darkness. He found one beside the fattening bullocks and hauled it back

114

into place. It took 20 minutes to find the second, see-sawing gently over a gate with a glazed look in its eyes and a dislocated shoulder. He walked it back to the stall, put a poultice on the shoulder and gave it a hiding for good measure.

Now there was nothing else for it. It would have to be him. He walked slowly along the shed to the furthest away stall knowing what he would find. Yes, there he was. Knock-kneed, skittering again, on the verge of pneumonia as usual, nose glowing like a beacon. Ruefully Santa Claus fitted a rusty harness onto Rudolph and led him back to the rest of the team.

He was going to sack this lot of fairies, pixies and elves and hire a mechanic. The first fat sale at Tyneside after Christmas, Rudolph and his mates were going for sausages. And he was going to buy a four wheel drive.

He stuck Rudolph in with the rest and gave him a penicillin injection as a precaution.

As reindeer and cart limped off into the darkness Santa pulled up his hood as far as he could and sank back into the seat. Drat this for a joke he thought. If he didn't get a four wheel drive with matching accessories for next Christmas he was finished. Definitely.

Talking turkey

'What are they up to now?'

'I don't know – it's hard to see in this light.'

'Never mind. They'll soon settle down again. They get all excited and make a lot of noise for a while then quieten down.'

'I hope so. That racket's giving me a headache. And my legs are hurting again.'

'What do you expect? You never stop. On the go all the time. Rushing here – rushing there. Checking the feeding. Checking that the water's running into the bowls. Making sure there's enough shavings.'

'Well, somebody's got to do it. I don't see you doing a lot.'

'Oh, I do enough to get by, don't you worry. I just don't see the point in running round like a blue-tailed fly to prove it. We all know how hard you work. You make enough noise about it.'

'Keep it civil, keep it civil. No point in losing your temper just because some of us are more conscientious than others. But I wish they'd stop making that noise. I think I'm going deaf.'

'There's one playing with a bit of rope now. Dragging it about and picking away at it like an idiot.'

'I tell you, you get your laughs in here. See that big one over there. I've often noticed him at feeding time. Running round all the feeders one after another, spilling feeding and making a noise.'

'And the time he fell over the bale and walked with a limp for a week? He's a comic, that one.'

'Funny enough, you never notice most of them. They all look alike, you know – have you realised that as well? It must be the modern breeding methods, I suppose.'

'They don't seem to have grown as fast this year. I always thought they'd be bigger by now.'

'Hard to tell really. Some of them are big enough – mind you, there's that little runty one that I've noticed occasionally. I think that's a genetic throwback.'

'A what?'

'A mistake in the breeding programme with its little bandy legs and funny shaped head and chest.'

'What are they doing now?'

'Well, the one with the bit of rope's still making a lot of noise and dragging it about. Oh dear, oh dear, oh dear – look at this. Did you ever see anything like that – he's got it wrapped round his legs now and fallen over.'

'I sometimes think they haven't got the sense to stand upright.'

'Well, that one hasn't. And the one next to him isn't much better. Poking away at the straw like that then banging away at a piece of wood. It makes you wonder how far evolution's come really.'

'Look – look! You're missing the best one with it's head in a bucket and it's backside in the air. What is it doing?'

'Your guess is as good as mine. I've given up trying to decide what makes them tick. I think there's just a big empty space where their brains should be.'

'Now they're squawking at each other again. There they go – hammer and tongs. They'll be at each other's throats any minute."

'No, there's the boss one getting stuck into them. I've noticed when that one starts pushing his weight about they quieten down.'

'I hope so. I can't take much of this. What are they all doing anyway – it never usually takes as long as this?'

'They're coming up to look through the wire now. Funny looking brutes aren't they really. That little one looks really miserable – no wonder, with those funny little legs and pointed head.'

'It would be interesting to know if they were actually saying anything to each other.'

'I don't think they've got the sense.'

117

'Oh, I don't know – see, they're really making a racket now with their heads up against the wire. My, they look sad – I think they're ready to burst into tears.'

'You're right. They probably wish they were in here with us turkeys.'

Welcome respite

For those who believe in it, there is obviously a place and a need for a Christmas festival and holiday. Religion doesn't come into it, but I suppose the same applies to Ne'erday.

Looked at rationally rather than through the fug of hype, sentiment, commercialism, works parties, and television, the whole idea seems to have got out of hand.

It's not so long ago that Christmas Day was still a working day for many of us. On livestock farms it still is, and I always think it adds a special flavour.

It is true that the flavour is not always to our liking. Two years running, ewes thought there was something special enough about the day to die on it.

Twice we've had to call out the vet to sick cattle. More than once, the day has been a battle with frozen water troughs, and more frequently a struggle with mud and wet and mild conditions.

But the morning livestock session is a breath of fresh air before the onslaught of children opening presents, the festive fare, and a warm radio. The afternoon session is almost equally welcome to work off the meal.

Christmas Day is off to a head start in our estimation anyway, because it is the first day for several months without turkeys. After months of feeding we have had about 10 days of plucking, cleaning, and delivering, right up to the collection of the last few orders on Christmas Eve.

Any left over, for whatever reason, have been put into the freezer, and the one for the dinner is basting nicely in the oven. There are only cattle and pigs to think about.

We usually make sure all stock have ample straw on Christmas Eve to get them through to Boxing Day, but one or two big bales still have to be dropped into feeders.

Barrow-loads of feeding are shovelled out into troughs along both sides of the big shed, where we have more than 140 cattle at present.

Even on Christmas Day there is time to ponder once more whether so many are a good thing or a bad thing.

It is a lot of money to have on four legs – or at least 140 by 4 legs – but will continue to appreciate faster than it would have done if we had sold the winter barley at harvest, sold the cattle as stores and calves, and slashed the overdraft into credit.

In the farrowing house there has been a change in temperature in the past three months, since we invested in roof insulation. Since we started a pig herd, costs have been kept to a minimum by using second-hand equipment bought cheaply or for the taking away, plus some block walling and metalwork on gates.

The drawback with fitting this into adapted buildings has been draughts and lower temperatures than small pigs find comfortable. Liberal use of straw helped, but it became clear that more insulation was necessary.

We decided on a spray-on type applied by a specialist firm. It goes on to the roof and walls as a foam which quickly hardens.

The resulting rise in temperature, even on the coldest days we have had this winter, has been surprising. Piglets spread themselves out comfortably on the straw rather than snuggling as close as possible to the sow for warmth, with the increased risk that she will flatten them.

A farrowing house of sows quietly suckling is a pleasant place to be on Christmas morning.

Some other parts are not so pleasant. We have had trouble with a blocked drain outside the new shed, which has caused some waterlogging and wading in the yard.

Clearing it is one of a long list of jobs carried forward into the New Year.

These include road repairs, gutter repairs, machinery maintenance, and tree planting to replace felled elms. The autumn disappeared after the late harvest, and the spring shows every sign of going the same way.

We could be drilling spring barley in a few weeks, given the right weather. On the other hand, it could be nearly four months.

Spring drilling and Boxing Day seem a long way apart. For many people, work of any kind and Boxing Day seem a long way apart, with the Christmas and New Year festivities merging into each other.

Farming, particularly livestock farming, doesn't give you the chance to fritter time away like that. I can't help feeling that if all work and no play makes Jack a dull boy, the converse is also true.

Game for a laugh

Many years ago there was a board game based on farming. It was called Agrihazard and we played a lot of it one Christmas.

I don't remember the intricacies of it, but there were various types of farm and various systems that could be followed.

Naturally, those of us who knew what to do tried to get the biggest farms with the most complicated arable systems and the maximum number of tractors.

The tractors came into it because the game was originally developed by Ford as part of a promotion campaign. If neighbours were unlucky enough to land on your squares, the rent or fine they had to pay was dictated by the number of tractors you had.

The bigger farms involved a lot of trading and decisions, because the game seemed reasonably realistic apart from the number of Ford tractors needed on a two hundred acre farm; this was probably wishful thinking by the sales team which had developed the game.

With several of us getting the bigger farms, my youngest brother – about 10 years-old at the time – invariably ended up with the 500 acre hill farm which even in the fevered minds of tractor salesmen only warranted two small Fords. If I remember correctly, he had a card which said he grew 100 acres of turnips and sold 400 lambs each year.

There were other progressive hill farming options, but he always refused to take them. While the rest of us threw dice in a frenzy trying to make money, he simply moved his counter round the board as the numbers came up, collecting his annual income from 400 lambs and occasionally getting the bonus of a load of shopping turnips.

It was useless to point out to him that he was simply sitting on his assets. Exhortations, threats, curses and occasional blows to the side of the head left him unmoved, if occasionally roaring. He was the most stick-in-the-mud farmer I ever played with.

What was really driving us insane, of course, was the fact that he kept winning. Each time round the board was a farming year and on the basis that skill and judgement was bound to tell in the end we sometimes kept the game going until the small hours of the morning waiting for him to crack.

Fortified only by the occasional orange juice while the beer cans and cigarette ends mounted round him, he sat on and on with a fixed smile, doing nothing except move his counter and collect his annual income.

He had one great advantage in that the number of hazards likely were fewer with his turnips and lambs; one or two chance cards such as 'Turnip crop wiped out by finger and toe' or 'Abortion storm three weeks before lambing' would have evened things up.

I think the worst that could happen to him was 'Last 10 acres drilled fail to germinate' while the rest of us were losing whole dairy herds by electrocution or 80 acres of wheat with yellow rust or £3,000 for a combine repair.

I was glad when we stopped playing the game and went on to Escape from Colditz instead; even Monopoly gave us more of a chance.

One Christmas another game reared up. Called simply Farming, it claims to be realistic. That claim may be true; the first game we played was won by a seven year old.

Unlike the late and unlamented Agrihazard, all farms in this game are the same size with the same livestock. Some choice is allowed on the 100 acres of arable though yields are a bit variable with a possible top of 30 cwt. for oats or an eye-watering 19 cwt. for wheat.

Players don't move round a board. Instead, the banker who is also the auctioneer, turns over the play cards. Each card represents a week in the farming year – more or less – and each farmer has to follow the instructions as they apply to him, or her.

123

It has its moments. The monthly wage bill must be met, feedstuffs paid for, farming hazards like poor farrowings and disease dealt with. Throw a one on the lambing card and your 50 ewes have 55 lambs and you lose five ewes; throw a six and you have 75 lambs with no losses. Decide for yourself which is the closest to reality.

In fact, the game lasted about two hours and I enjoyed it. This was not because I came second to the seven year old or anything like that. I enjoyed it because I have learned a little in the years between Agrihazard and Farming.

I have learned that being a banker or an auctioneer looks like more fun. Acting as both together was too good a chance to miss. There may be more counting and calculations to do, but the pleasure of handling all that money belonging to other players compensates for it. And, oh, that feeling of power.

A deadly pecking order . . .

Right, pay attention you lot. No cheeping and pecking at the back there – plenty of time for that later on. We haven't got long – they're going to come back soon and find we've got through the wire. Hoi, you at the side – what the devil do you think you're doing?

Eating! Eating to keep healthy and growing? What do you think this is, sonny – a holiday camp? A health farm? You should cocoa. I never heard anything like it. Eyes front you horrible little feathered freak – tenshun!

And you in the middle – yes, you, the one that looks as if you should have been an omlette. Don't just stand there – peck your neighbour. You can't get into the swing of things too quickly.

Why? Why what? Why should you peck him? Oh dear, oh dear, oh dear – what are they sending out from the hatcheries these days, I ask myself. It would bring tears to my old mother's eyes, bless her wing feathers and wishbone.

Get stuck in lad. Have a go. That's it, back of the head – jab, jab. Promising, son, very promising. A few dozen like that and he'll be to carry out. Go on, that's it, peck him back.

You, you and you – pecking detail. Pick on him at the end and keep at him. Why? Because I'm telling you that's why – that should be good enough for you. One, two, three – peck.

Right, the rest of you – poults, month-old, 100, Christmas dinners for the use of. The trick is to see how many of you avoid reaching mid-December. Now pecking is one way – pecking each other to death is definitely in order – keep at it, you lot, don't let him get out of that corner.

Never mind if he's cheeping. It means he's enjoying having his head caved in. Yes, he's allowed to peck back – that's half the fun.

But there are other ways just as good. That's why we've nipped through the wire – nice little hole there, might hang myself on it as we go back – to pass on a few tricks of the trade from old stagers. Claws up anybody who has any ideas – come on, month old poults must have a few ideas about doing yourself or another bird in?

Who's that holding up both feet? Is he? Really? Stone dead? Very good. That really is very good. Well done that man. We'll recommend him for a posthumous award – dead, just like that within four hours of arrival. I like it. Drowning? Who cheeped drowning? Quite right, good thinking. Now this chap's a bit clever, its small automatic drinkers, you can hardly get your beak in never mind drown.

But occasionally there's a bucket of water left sitting outside the pen. It's tricky, but it has been done – five of us managed to get out through the netting and climb into the bucket.

Drown? Of course they drowned. That was the whole idea. Wake up there! But once was probably enough – they haven't left the bucket again I notice. Still, keep your eyes and options open, never know your luck.

Shavings? Yes, not bad, bit slow and messy, but can be done. Stuff yourself with shavings instead of feed and explode. Volunteers one two – start stuffing.

No, you're not supposed to like the taste – just keep swallowing. Bales – yes, good. Bales are about my favourite I would say. They can never be sure with bales. They're so useful, you see, for blocking off draughts, blocking doorways, spreading on the floor.

And no matter how careful they think they're being – well, I ask you. Keep your eye on the bales – as soon as you see one ready to fall, get fell in. Any falling bale must be good for at least one passing out parade. Good one, eh? Passing out.

It's the look on their faces that kills me – not if I can help it, of course. I'll be gone long before they can get their hands on me. But it's the look when they lift the bale and find one of us underneath – flat and peaceful. Oh, it's worth waiting for I'll tell you. And think – it could be you doing your bit for the cause.

So – to recap. Pecking, drowning, shavings, bales. Sudden death caused by mind over matter as with our feet in the air friend here. What else – come on, now, let's have a bit of initiative.

Hanging – good. Can be achieved in several ways. Netting is well worth trying. String left over from the bales worth a thought. Jamming your head behind the door as it opens – yes, possible, but tricky.

Heart attacks in mid-December really crack them up, but it's cutting it fine. You can miscalculate at that stage. But – oh, oh, trouble. Here comes one of them. Watch this for a spectacular leap and choke – remember what I've told you – here goes . . . agh . . .

Brand new boots . . .

When the cow with the soft brown eyes kicked the milk bucket over for the third time, lashed him across the forehead with the sodden end of her tail and trampled heavily on his left foot with her dainty little hooves, he thought of milk bottles and steak pie.

It would really be cheaper to buy six pints a day, he thought as he twisted her tail round her leg to stop her kicking. And if he'd thought of it sooner, £80 from a dealer to turn her into tinned steak pie would have been very handy before Christmas.

Well, well, he mused as he sat down again on the four-legged stool with only three legs, rammed his head into the hollow of her bony hip and tried to strip off another pint or two of milk while holding her tail between his clenched knees and swearing softly through his clenched teeth: well, well, another good idea too late.

'Well I'll be damned,' he said, as the tail disappeared from between his knees and rattled his left ear in one flowing movement. He managed to save the bucket, knock over the stool, cast his eyes to heaven and give her a half hearted kick in the ribs to complete his part of the double act performed twice daily.

He turned to leave the byre then grunted to himself, came back, and jammed another clump of hay into the manger. 'Enjoy it, it may be your last,' he muttered, then for some reason he patted her on the neck. The cow tossed her head then went back muzzle-deep into the hay.

He trudged across the yard, the occasional pointed stone reminding him that he needed a new pair of wellingtons. Maybe he should have sent in the request to S. Claus, Greenland, along with the children. Ah, Christmas was a good time for them.

When he reached the kitchen, two of them were engaged in a friendly discussion. It was a slightly one-sided discussion as the nine-year-old had the five-year-old in a full Nelson and the five-year-old was bawling festive greetings at the top of his voice.

Thornton separated them with a festive clip on the ear, reassured the five-year-old that Santa wasn't dead, glared threateningly at the nine-year-old, then did a swift Ali shuffle back into the yard in his muddy wellingtons as his wife pointed out icily that she had just washed the kitchen floor.

It had been that sort of day, he thought bitterly, as he turned the milk separator in the back kitchen, watching the stream of white milk hit the basin and the thick flow of yellow cream trickle into the jug.

From the time he had found 200 lambs on the turnips after breaking down the net in the morning to the time the house-cow had kicked the bucket for the third time at six o'clock at night, it had been that sort of day.

Of course, he thought, when you spend most of a day plucking turkeys you can't expect much else. You buy 100 chicks in summer to give you a bit of ready cash at Christmas: you dose them against every turkey disease known to man and you invent a new one: you try to keep them warm and they pile up five deep in the only draughty corner: you try to feed them and they won't eat: you give them water and they try to drown themselves.

Worse than sheep, he muttered as the last of the cream trickled into the jug. But what happened to all those fluffy little suicides when it came to Christmas?

I'll tell you, he said to himself, as he tiptoed cautiously into the kitchen in his stockinged feet. It's the survival of the fittest, and the ones that are left have turned into 25lb feathered furies with claws like razors and a wing-spread like an albatross.

Lion tamers, he snorted as he put the cream in the fridge: I'd take lion taming any time. I'd like to see them going into a pen of 80 turkeys and stretching a few necks.

Well, it was over for another year. Well, almost. The four-year-old and the seven-year-old were having a heated argument about who would get a pony and who would be the most surprised.

I will, he muttered, very surprised, if a cowboy outfit and a tricycle turn into a pony overnight. Oh blast! He'd forgotten to bed down the 20 bullocks in the top courting.

I wonder how far you'd have to carry a bale of straw before it finally disappeared, he thought gloomily as he walked across the yard with a bale in each hand, leaving a trail of golden straw in the starlight.

Good straw, though, clean and crisp and dry, not like the sodden mouldy stuff from last harvest. He shook out the six bales with a fork, the cattle lying placidly watching him undisturbed. At least something's contented round here he thought as he shut the gate behind him.

He leaned on the gate for a few minutes, watching them, inhaling the pleasant smell of well-fed cattle on fresh straw. He always found it difficult to stop his jaws moving up and down in time with the beasts as they chewed the cud.

It was a mild night and he was alone in the starlight. For no good reason he found himself smiling as he looked upwards again.

'Don't forget the wellingtons,' he murmured as he set off across the yard towards the light in the kitchen window.